D0049263

HAUNTED HIGHWAYS

HAUNTED HIGHWAYS

Spooky Stories, Strange Happenings,
and Supernatural Sightings

Retold by Tom Ogden

BRISTOL PARK BOOKS / NEW YORK

For family—Nancy, Albert, Jeanne, and Linda.

First Bristol Park Books edition published in 2011

Published by Bristol Park Books
252 W. 38th Street
NYC, NY 10018

Bristol Park Books is a registered trademark of Bristol Park Books, Inc.

Published by arrangement with The Globe Pequot Press

Library of Congress Cataloging-in Publication Data is available on file.

ISBN: 978-0-88486-487-5

Printed in the United States of America

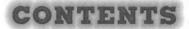

CONTENTS

ACKNOWLEDGMENTS

My thanks go out to Shawn McMaster for sharing his ghost-hunting adventure on Creek Road outside Ojai, California, and Michael Kurland for turning me on to the story of Benjamin Bathurst, the vanishing traveler. Also, I have to thank David Shine for acting as a sounding board and for sharing his ideas as I obsessed over every story.

Finally, special thanks have to go to my editor Mary Norris and project manager Jennifer Taber, as well as Gary Krebs, who first recommended me for the project and has continued his enthusiasm and support over these many years.

INTRODUCTION

Boo!

Are you ready for some really spooky tales of ghosts, supernatural creatures, and things that go bump in the night? If so, turn down the lights, curl up under the covers, and get ready to be scared as twenty-five of the most famous highway hauntings of all times unfold before your eyes.

All of the ghost stories in this collection are based on ancient myths and urban legends—tales that have been told and retold through the centuries. Every story has something in common: All have occurred on or near a highway, street, trail, or other pathway.

What you're about to read are actual sightings. In some cases I've taken the basic account and fictionalized the story by adding secondary characters for dramatic purposes, but for all intents and purposes the story is the one that's been passed down through the ages.

What makes this book possible is that ghosts haunt *places,* not *people.* That's why you'll read here about hauntings that recur on a particular roadway. The spirits are coming back to a specific street or path to relive or deal with an event from their own lives, not to interfere with the living who encounter them. In fact, almost without exception, the people who bump into ghosts have no clue as to their identity. (So if you run into a ghost out there on the street, you should probably apologize: You've interrupted *them,* not the other way around.)

Which brings up an interesting point: If you do encounter one of these spirits, should you be afraid of it? Well, yes and no. People always fear the unknown. But one of the most common misconceptions about ghosts—no doubt promulgated by what you see in the movies—is that spirits return from the grave to terrorize the living. Surprisingly, however, there are almost no examples throughout history of ghosts deliberately trying to hurt people. A few cases have been reported in which a spectre has returned to impart a message or a warning, but rarely, if ever, do ghosts hurt anyone. They're certainly not out to get you!

You may be surprised to discover that not all of the spirits that you find in this book are "ghosts" at all, at least not in the usual sense. That is to say, they don't all fit the popular, narrow definition of a ghost as the returning soul or essence of a deceased human.

Rather, some of the best-known haunted tales in history, including several found in this book, involve apparitions such as animals (like the horse ridden by the Headless Horseman), noises (such as the sound of invisible car crashes), or—and this is especially relevant to the subject of *Haunted Highways*—vehicles (such as phantom cars, trains, or stagecoaches).

There were, of course, thousands of wonderful, terrifying stories to choose from, so selecting which ones to retell was difficult. After all, accounts of phantom travelers have appeared in western literature since at least the seventeenth century, and they no doubt were passed down as oral tradition long before that.

There have been so many sightings of ghost hitchhikers, for example, that I could have filled an entire book with accounts of them alone. Instead, I've collected a wide variety of tales representing different types of hauntings, and I've separated them into four *very* loose categories.

All of the ghosts in the first section of this book are, indeed, variations of the archetypical vanishing hitchhiker story in which a spirit that thumbs a ride along a deserted path late at night is picked up by a helpful stranger and then disappears without a trace from the car. The stories in Part Two tell about ghosts that roam a particular street or path. The third section involves spirits that are doomed to return to Earth to relive a particular event in their lives. And the last part contains a cacophony of spectres whose lives were cut short due to accident, execution, or injustice. To cap it all off, I've ended with the ghosts that haunt the highway with the most notorious-sounding name of all: Route 666, nicknamed the Highway to Hell.

I've also added three helpful appendices at the back of the book to help you learn more about the stories and legends:

"'BOO'k Reports" is a descriptive bibliography of the works I consulted while researching the stories contained in *Haunted Highways* as well as a representative sampling of some of the hundreds of other books on the subject. I've also listed some of the premier Web sites on ghosts and hauntings that can be found on the Internet.

"Ghost Hunting" gives the addresses, telephone contact, or directions to many of the haunted places mentioned in this book, broken down by chapter. Unless otherwise noted, most are open to the public or welcome your business patronage.

"Ghost Notes" provides background information and context for several of the ghost stories. In addition, you'll find many more short ghost tales related to the ones already featured in the book.

Part One

VANISHING HITCHHIKERS

As we start our journey along some of the most haunted highways of the world, let's first take a look at the mother of all such ghost stories: the legend of the phantom hitchhiker, spirits who either hitch or accept a ride, only to later disappear from the vehicle, to the driver's shock and dismay.

Shiver as you read the stories of Resurrection Mary, who revisits her flight from the Oh Henry Ballroom outside Chicago; the phantom nun who, for more than a year, ominously predicted the imminent eruption of Mount St. Helens; and La Llorna, the Weeping Woman who grieves for her lost and murdered children.

Chapter 1
The Phantom Hitchhiker

They say that no good deed goes unpunished. And that's certainly true if you're not careful when you give a hitchhiker a lift. If you're on a haunted highway, that stranger you pick up may be a lot stranger than you think!

Fortunately, Jonathan wasn't in a hurry. He could get there by tomorrow morning if he pressed himself and drove all the way through the night. But he had started to fade about an hour back, so he knew that, if only for safety's sake, it would be better if he stopped somewhere along the way and continued on in the morning.

He tried all the usual tricks to stay awake. But coffee didn't seem to be having any effect. He rode with the window open, despite the chill in the late September air, hoping that the wind whipping in his face would keep him alert. Instead, it just had him blinking his eyes more often. He had turned the radio up and was singing along—loudly—to songs he barely knew. He had even started talking to himself, taking both parts in an almost-comical Q&A.

"So, where are you heading this late at night?"

"Oh, I promised to visit my parents."

"Not the parents! Don't you see them enough?"

"Well, I talk to them every couple of days. Okay, every couple of weeks."

But it had been several months—oh, my God, had it been more than a year?—since Jonathan had been home. He'd been busy. His parents knew that, and they were happy for him for making a new life, rather successfully if Jonathan had to say so himself. Of course, he couldn't really be happy, according to his mom, until he found a nice girl and settled down. Maybe she was right. Maybe it *was* time for him to settle down. To meet a . . .

A girl! Were his eyes playing tricks? It was after ten o'clock, and yet there, standing alone on the side of the road just ahead of him, seemed to be a girl of about eighteen.

Suddenly, he saw the curve. The highway had been running in a straight line along the river for the last hour, and then here, coming out of nowhere, was a sharp bend in the road. He pressed on his brakes, quickly cutting his speed. The car slowed to a manageable crawl just as the road began to turn. Why, if he hadn't seen the girl standing in the middle of the bend, he might have missed the curve and continued straight off the highway. He would have plunged into the river. She'd probably saved his life!

But where was she? He had just seen her. He knew he had. He pulled off onto the narrow shoulder and heard the gravel crunching beneath his tires. He stopped the engine but left the lights on. This far outside of town, with no street lamps and no other traffic on the deserted highway, it was almost pitch black. He stepped outside to look around.

There wasn't any wind, and yet he felt a small breeze on the back of his neck. He shivered as his flesh broke out in goose bumps. Odd: It felt as if the temperature had somehow instantly dropped about ten degrees. Slowly he became uncomfortably aware that someone or something was standing right behind him. He turned and found himself face-to-face with the girl.

She was beautiful. She stood about five-seven, with straight brown hair just touching the shoulders of her long, white linen dress. Her complexion was pale, but flawless, and her clear eyes sparkled in the car's headlights.

"Oh!" Jonathan cried out in surprise. "You scared me. Well, not scared, exactly. It's just that, I didn't expect to see you, anyone, I mean . . . " He caught his breath, and then, composed, introduced himself. "My name's Jonathan. Are you walking? It's miles until the next town. Can I offer you a ride?"

It was then that Jonathan noticed the girl was soaking wet. A small puddle of water, in fact, had gathered around her bare feet. She must be freezing.

"Here, please, get in the car. It's warm. And put this around yourself. You'll catch a cold." Jonathan slipped off his sport coat and draped it around the girl's shoulders.

Quietly, she moved to the car, gliding so effortlessly that he didn't even hear the stones against her feet. The girl opened the back door and slid into the middle of the seat. Jonathan didn't object. Maybe she was afraid to sit up front so close to someone she didn't know, no matter how harmless he appeared to be. Instinctively, he knew this wasn't going to be a chatty evening.

He started up the engine as he looked over his shoulder. "Where are you heading?"

She gave him an address in the town about ten miles down the road. He only vaguely remembered seeing the name of the street the last time he had driven through, but he figured she'd be able to direct him once they got closer.

Jonathan glanced up into the rearview mirror. The girl had closed her eyes and seemed to be humming softly to herself, even though he couldn't hear any sound. He noticed that she had gathered the jacket around herself, so he reached over and turned up the heater. How had she gotten so wet? he wondered. It hadn't rained all night. Had she gone down to the riverbank for some reason and accidentally fallen in?

He had little time to think about it, though, before he saw the cross street. He turned and made his way slowly down the road, straining to see the house numbers painted on the curb. Most of the homes were dark. It was, after all, getting very late. Most people had gone to bed by this time of night.

Then, up ahead, he saw a house standing a little farther back from the edge of the sidewalk, its downstairs lights blazing. That must be it. Someone was probably up waiting. Jonathan wondered if it was her parents, worried sick the way he knew his parents would be. Or what if it was a boyfriend or even her husband? He hadn't thought about that!

Jonathan saw the address on the mailbox at the end of the drive and stopped out on the street rather than pulling into the driveway. It had occurred to him that the circumstances might seem rather suspicious. A girl, alone at night, no vehicle, miles out of town, soaking wet from who knows what. He was happy to help out someone in trouble, but he hadn't even asked her why she was out there all on her own; and she hadn't offered an explanation. There was no reason to get any more involved now.

The girl was so quiet that Jonathan was sure she had gone to sleep. He looked into the mirror. Where was she?

Had she stretched out on the backseat? He turned to look over his shoulder. "We're here," he called jokingly. "Rise and shine!" But she was gone!

No, that was impossible. It couldn't be! Had she slipped down onto the floor? No, not there either. He quickly glanced from side to side. The car doors were still locked. Besides, he would have heard something if she had opened the car while they were moving. How could she have gotten out?

He couldn't believe his own eyes. Had he been hallucinating, or dreaming? He knew he had been falling asleep at the wheel before he picked her up. Maybe he had imagined the whole thing. He reached behind him and felt the empty car seat. He jerked back his hand as if he had been shocked by a jolt of electricity. The car seat was still damp.

Then he remembered his jacket. He had given her his sport coat to keep warm. He knew he had been wearing the jacket when he started out from home, and he wasn't wearing it now. It wasn't on the seat beside him, and it wasn't on the back seat either. She must have taken it with her— wherever she went.

Jonathan jumped out of the car and walked all the way around it. He looked down the narrow asphalt road, one way, then the other. There was no trace of the girl. She had simply disappeared! Like a ghost.

He stood there, confused, at a complete loss as to what to do next. He looked across the newly mown lawn up to the house. He didn't want to bother strangers, especially close to midnight, but she *had* given this address. And the lights were still on. Maybe whoever lived there had some answers.

Quietly he walked up to the doorstep. He raised his hand, paused slightly, and then made up his mind and knocked on the door. The porch light snapped on almost instantly, startling him. He regained his composure as the door opened slowly. Greeting him was a woman of about forty-five, with prematurely white hair, and calm, comforting eyes. Several feet over her shoulder, Jonathan could make out a man of about the same age, perhaps a bit older, head downcast.

"We've been expecting you," the woman said softly. "Please come in."

"You've been expecting me?"

"Or someone like you. Please. Come in. "

Jonathan hesitated. What was he getting himself into?

As if to answer his unspoken question, the woman gently prompted, "Tell me, did you . . . did you meet a girl on the road tonight?"

Jonathan was dumbstruck. How could she have known why he was there or what had happened? Before he could ask, the woman opened the door wider, gestured inside, and said, "Let us explain."

Jonathan allowed himself to be ushered into the room. Comfortable. Well kept. He sat on one end of the sofa and the woman settled next to him. She drew a photo album onto her lap. "I'll explain everything you want to know. But first, please take a look at these. Is this the girl you met?"

He flipped slowly through the pages. Yes, that was the girl who had been in his car. There were dozens of pictures taken of her over the years, from the time she was starting grade school, during her teen years, right up to the age she must be now.

"Yes. That's her. But, then, she must be one of your family."

"Yes. That's Jeanne. She was our daughter."

Was? Jonathan's mind started to race. Then the girl he picked up, the one who got into his car, the one who vanished, was no longer alive?

"Yes. That was our little girl. Well, not so little. She was almost nineteen. She died just five years ago. Five years ago tonight."

At that, Jonathan lost it. It couldn't be, he screamed to himself. She couldn't be dead. Not if he had just seen her, talked with her. That sort of thing just doesn't happen. Not in the real world.

"Five years ago she was driving home from a party, late at night, on that road along the river that you must have been following into town. There was a light rain that night, the first after a long dry spell, so the roads would have been slick. We don't really know what happened, whether she fell asleep at the wheel, whether something jumped out in the road in front of her and she lost control. Maybe she was just going a little too fast. But there was that big curve—you must have noticed it, most of the road is as straight as a line—and the car crashed through the guardrail."

The mother paused and turned slightly toward her husband who was sitting quietly on the other side of the room. "Have they ever replaced that, honey?" She seemed lost in her thoughts. "I don't think they ever did."

She looked back at the young man. "Anyway, her car went right into the river. They said that she was probably knocked unconscious. It didn't look as if she even tried to get out of the car . . . "

Her voice trailed off. The three sat in silence. Jonathan looked around the room. How hadn't he noticed when he first came in? There were pictures of the girl everywhere. On the wall. In the stairwell. There was her high school graduation photo, in cap and gown, on the mantle over the fireplace. He stared blankly as the mind-numbing truth sank in.

For the first time, Jeanne's father spoke, his voice startling Jonathan.

"She's buried over at St. Matthew's. You can see for yourself if you're staying in town. Her picture's on the marker. Lots of people are doing that now, putting a photo on the headstone. It helps you remember when you visit. To remember them, the way it was. It's not supposed to be like this, you know. The parents are supposed to go first." The words caught in his throat.

His wife picked up the train of thought. "She was our only child. We knew we would never stop thinking about her; we do every day. But we thought it would get easier. Then it started.

"A year after she died, a year to the day of the accident, a young man, a man much like you, came to our front door. He told us this incredible story. He had picked up a hitchhiker. A girl. She had given him this address. Then she had disappeared. Of course, what were we to think? How cruel could someone be? Who hated us so much that they would play such a sick joke on us? Of course, we sent him away. I'm sorry to say now that we slammed the door in his face. Told him to get off our property before we called the police. Then it happened again the next year. A different man.

"I don't know. Maybe it was because another year had gone by. A little more time to forget. Anyway, this time we listened to the whole story—where it was that he first saw the girl, right at that bend in the road. I'm guessing it was the same with you. She was soaking wet, for no apparent reason. And she didn't offer to explain why or how she had gotten there. But she gave our address."

Jonathan broke in quietly. "Yes. She opened the door and slid into the backseat. Like you said, she was wet. I gave her my jacket to keep her warm. She didn't say much, just asked me to take her here. I didn't pry. I just wanted to help out."

Jeanne's mother gently reached out her hand and laid it on top of Jonathan's. "I think she appeared to you because she knew she'd be safe. She was a very good judge of character. All of the others, the other four, they all seemed like such nice young men."

Embarrassed, Jonathan picked up the story. "I glanced up into the rearview mirror from time to time. Just to check, you know. She had closed her eyes, seemed to be drifting off to sleep. When I pulled up in front of your house, I looked over my shoulder and, well, she was gone. I didn't know what to do. I saw that your light was on, so I took a chance."

Quiet invaded the room. After a few minutes, Jeanne's parents stood up. Jonathan knew it was time to go. The girl's father shook Jonathan's hand and, on an impulse, her mother gave him a quick hug. "We've never seen her, you know. As often as we've driven that road in all the years since. After we heard the story a second time, after we believed, we always hoped we would. Well, maybe it's better this way. Thank you for helping our little girl."

They still missed her—*this* much, after five full years. She would have been twenty-three if she were still alive. But they still thought of her as their "little girl." *I guess you're always a kid to your parents,* thought Jonathan. He made a mental note to be extra kind to his parents when he got home the next day.

And with that, the girl's folks showed Jonathan to the door. The hour had gotten late, so he decided to make his overnight break there and pulled into a motel at the far edge of town.

The next morning, he awoke with a start. The events of the night before crowded into his mind. Had they really happened? They must have. Otherwise, he would be a hundred more miles down the road like he had planned. After a quick shower, it was time to get back on the highway. As he checked out at the front desk, he had a sudden whim and asked the clerk, "Do you know where St. Matthew's Church is located?"

Armed with directions, Jonathan set off for the simple Lutheran church. He pulled into the empty parking lot. There, to one side, was a short path leading to the cemetery in the back. He walked through the open iron gate and quickly scanned the tombstones. He was looking for one that would be relatively new, one with a small photograph set into the stone. There it was!

He slowly walked over to the headstone. As he looked down, a smiling face beamed back to him from the marker. That was definitely the girl.

And then he noticed it. At first he had just dismissed it as a flag or perhaps a work cloth left behind by a caretaker. But there, neatly folded and draped over one end of the tombstone, was a blue sport jacket. It was his, the one he had offered the trembling hitchhiker the night before. To thank him for his kindness, Jeanne had returned his coat from beyond the grave.

Chapter 2

Resurrection Mary

Sometimes it's too much to ask a spirit to stay put, especially if she loves to dance. Take the case of Resurrection Mary, whose ghost often appears on the wooded stretch of highway between the ballroom that, in life, she used to frequent and the cemetery in which she now rests for eternity. If you give a ride to a hitchhiker some night outside Chicago, you might just meet her.

What Depression? As Mary danced away the wintry night with her boyfriend and hundreds of others on the hardwood floor of the ballroom at Oh Henry Park that night in 1939, the economic hardships of the preceding decade seemed a distant memory.

Even the dance halls had changed. The desperate, week-long dance marathons were gone. It was the Jazz Age, with couples throwing away their cares and worries while swinging to the big bands. From dusk almost to dawn, the music transported the crowd to a world of fantasy and illusion, far away from the drab, dull lives waiting for them back on the other side of the ballroom's doors.

Mary was new to the Oh Henry. But her date had promised her it was the hottest place to be on a Saturday night—even if the more established clubs of downtown Chicago were only fifteen miles away. In fact, there were almost four hundred ballroom and dance halls within an hour's drive of the Loop. But she had to admit it: the Oh Henry Ballroom was amazing.

Twenty years earlier, nothing had stood on the site. In 1921, Austrian immigrant John Verderbar bought five acres of land along that part of State Highway 171, known locally as Archer Avenue. He had intended to build a summer home on the property, but his high-spirited young son Rudy convinced him to construct an outdoor dancing pavilion instead. From the time the open-air dance hall opened as Oh Henry Park—the Williamson Candy Company, which manufactured the Oh Henry candy bar, reportedly paid for the naming rights—the place became a magnet for young people.

The original building was destroyed in a fire nine years later. But the new hall that rose from the ashes, the one in which Mary was now dancing, was bigger and better than before. Thousands of people made their way there each and every week to dance, meet friends, and listen to the bands.

The strains of "Over Somebody Else's Shoulder" wafted from the bandstand. Mary looked up to see the petite vocalist, Harriet Hillard, singing as she flirted with the bandleader who had introduced the song, her husband, Ozzie Nelson. His group was a favorite here at the Oh Henry, especially since Nelson had scored a number-one hit single with "And Then Some." It made Mary smile to see Ozzie and Harriet together, a couple who were obviously so much in love. Just like her and . . .

Where was he? Her boyfriend had offered to get them something to drink—they had been dancing nonstop for almost an hour—and he said he would be right back. But that was fifteen, no, twenty minutes ago! It wasn't like him to leave her all alone for so long.

She pressed her way across the dance floor, slowly working her way toward the bar. And then she saw him. He was *not* alone. Mary stood speechless as she saw her boyfriend pressed up against the girl he had dated before he met Mary. He had a sly, playful smile on his face and was whispering into her ear.

Stunned, Mary couldn't believe her own eyes. He had told her how difficult the breakup with the other girl had been, what an "evil" person she was, and how he never wanted to see her again. But now that Mary thought about it, her "boyfriend" did nothing *but* talk about his ex-girlfriend. And here he was, grinning and holding her hand!

She didn't wait for an explanation. She turned on her heels and, in a daze, headed straight to the door and stumbled outside. She was blocks away from the ballroom before she even realized she had left the building—without her coat in the middle of winter.

What was she going to do? Walk home? Well, she could do it. It was only three miles back to her parents' house in Justice. And with this brisk weather, why, she had every reason to move quickly. If she was lucky, maybe someone she knew would be leaving the dance hall, see her on the side of the road, and give her a ride.

Walking down the shoulder of the street, Mary was lost in her own thoughts as the truck approached from behind. Perhaps the driver's mind was somewhere else, too, or maybe he was nodding off at such a late hour. Otherwise, he might have seen Mary sooner. By the time his eye caught a flash of white—her dress—she had drifted onto the roadway. He slammed on the brakes . . .

Mary was buried a few days later in Resurrection Cemetery, just east of Justice. Her parents dressed her all in white, wearing her favorite dance shoes, the ones she had worn the very night she died.

✛

Setting out from Joliet just after 1 a.m., there was little traffic on the highway. Still, Jerry had to be careful. There were lots of people living in the area, and the road wasn't well lit once it got outside the city. As he passed through Lockport, State Road turned into Archer Avenue, and he followed it through Sag Bridge heading toward Chicago Midway Airport.

Jerry had been on the road for about a half hour when he entered the town of Willow Springs. The legal limits of Chicago had grown to within ten miles of the sleepy town, but it might as well have been in another world. Only six thousand people lived in Willow Springs. The city hadn't grown much from its heyday in the 1940s, when so many people flocked to the doors of the fabled Oh Henry Ballroom that there had been direct bus service there from midtown Chicago.

And there it was. Jerry knew the place only from its storied past. He had never been inside. The fact that it even still existed more than seventy years after it had opened its doors was a miracle. In its time, everyone had played the Oh Henry: Count Basie, Harry James, Jimmy Dorsey, Glenn Miller, Guy Lombardo. A who's who of big bands could have been compiled right there in the dance hall's dressing room.

Of course, the ballroom was no longer called the Oh Henry. As the swing era came to an end, other dance halls throughout the country closed their doors, but the Verderbar family expanded. They added on a kitchen, a restaurant, and banquet rooms, transforming the Oh Henry into an event facility they renamed the Willowbrook Ballroom. Tastes in music changed, and the next two decades brought such acts as Chubby Checker, the Association, and the Village People to its stage. Yeah, thought Jerry, the dancers who crammed into the ballroom to hear the big bands of yesteryear probably wouldn't even recognize the place.

Jerry peered through the dark. Was that a light by the side of the road up ahead? No, it was simply his own headlights reflecting off . . . a dress! Someone was walking out here? Alone? At this time of night?

With the person now in the full beam of his lights, Jerry could see the back of what appeared to be a slim young woman walking on the right shoulder of the road. Did he say walking? Her feet looked like they were barely touching the ground. She almost seemed to be floating.

Jerry pulled up beside the waiflike figure and rolled down the passenger-side window. He could see the moonlight reflecting off her ivory skin. She was dressed in a plain, white sleeveless dress, and long blond hair fell loosely over her shoulders. And even though it was summer, she was shivering.

"Pardon me. I don't want to bother you," he called out. "But could I be of some help? I thought you might need a lift somewhere."

The young woman stopped but didn't look his way.

"I promise I'm not an ax murderer or anything. I won't hurt you." Jerry laughed nervously at his own joke. Well, he thought, if that possibility hadn't already crossed her mind, she was certainly thinking it now. "Really. I just want to help. You look lost. And cold."

The girl turned to face the open window. She suddenly seemed to wake from a dream, and her face—especially the welcoming blue eyes focused on him—seemed filled with trust.

"Oh," she said, as if surprised to hear her own voice. "A lift. That would be nice."

She quietly opened the front door and slipped into the seat beside Jerry. Without another word, she settled back and stared out at the blackness on the other side of the windshield.

"Where are you headed?"

"Oh, I'm going home. It's just down the road. Straight ahead a few miles." And then, to answer his unspoken question as to what she was doing out there, she added, "I was dancing."

"Dancing? You mean at the Willowbrook?"

"Willowbrook? No, I don't know the Willowbrook. I was at the Oh Henry."

Puzzled, Jerry said nothing. The girl was obviously confused. The ballroom he'd just passed hadn't been called the Oh Henry since it was remodeled back in the '50s.

"It's one of my favorite places," she explained. "There's the music, of course. And the ballroom is full of life. I always have so much fun there." She sat motionless, her eyes wide, as if she were seeing the scene replaying in her mind. "I love to dance."

Jerry couldn't help but follow her eyes as she gazed down at her long, slender legs. On each foot was a spotless, soft, comfortable leather flat. The shoes were perfect if you wanted to stay light on your feet for hours at a time on a polished wooden dance floor.

She looked up abruptly. She met Jerry's eyes and smiled.

"I was there all night. The people wouldn't let the band stop playing. I danced and I danced. Sometimes just by myself. But tonight so many men asked me to join them, well, I just couldn't say no."

Tonight? Funny, thought Jerry. The lights had been out when he passed the Willowbrook. Of course, he didn't really know the club, but very few places stayed open this late, way out here in the suburbs. After all, it was after two. By this hour, most things were closed, even on the weekends.

Jerry wondered how long she had been walking. "You know, it's really none of my business. But it's rather unusual to see a woman out here all alone this late at night. Shouldn't you be, well, isn't there someone who could have driven you home?"

"Oh, there was. Once. But that was a long time ago. I've forgotten him." Had Jerry noticed a brief flash of anger on her face at the memory? "Now I like to go to the Oh Henry by myself. I can dance with anyone I please. And besides, I don't need him. I have *you* to drop me off. My Good Samaritan."

"Well, whoever the guy was, he must be crazy to have let you out of his sight."

He realized that he was flirting and panicked. He had *promised* her he was not a creep. But he couldn't stop himself. "What's your name?"

"Mary. Just Mary."

"That's a pretty name." Stop it, thought Jerry. "I mean, that name, you don't hear it very often these days."

"That's all right," Mary reassured him. "It *is* a pretty name." She was flirting back! "At least my parents didn't give me something awful like Edith or Myrtle."

"Now, wait a minute," Jerry joked, "I have an Aunt Myrtle."

They broke out in a soft laugh. Then, as they both became aware their conversation was becoming a bit too intimate for complete strangers, Mary shyly turned her face to the side window.

"I'm sorry. Where did you say you needed to go?"

"Home," Mary quietly reminded him. "Just on the other side of town."

They were approaching the outskirts of Justice even as she spoke. The car crossed Route 12, passed under I-294, and then slipped into the city. The sidewalks were empty as they passed through the center of town.

"Keep going. A little farther. It's just ahead."

Silence fell between them as they drove out of the city. Businesses thinned out, and they were back in a residential area. Her place must be coming up soon, thought Jerry.

"Stop!" Mary's call had come out of the blue. There were no houses nearby, just a park, an open field, a—was that a cemetery? Jerry eased his car to the side of the road and stopped the engine.

"Here. I have to get out here." Mary opened her door and stepped outside.

Jerry jumped out of the car. "Is something wrong? Mary? There's nothing here. I can drop you off at your house, even if it's a little out of the way. I mean, I don't mind." Was she afraid to let him know where she lived?

But Jerry's words had fallen on deaf ears. Mary had made a beeline across the field and was standing in front of a set of high greenish metal gates set between tall concrete pillars. Through the bars, Jerry could see a large mausoleum and hundreds of gravestones. To one side of the entrance was a small sign: Resurrection Cemetery.

For what, to Jerry, seemed like forever, Mary stood there in front of the gates. Then she made one small step forward and literally melted through the locked bars. Riveted to the spot, Jerry stared silently in a mixture of wonder and horror. She was now definitely on the other side of closed gates! Mary looked over her shoulder and found Jerry. A small, sad smile crossed her lips. She turned back into the cemetery as her body started to shimmer, then turned translucent. Slowly, her delicate shape began to fade until it completed evaporated into the cool, night air.

Mary was home.

Chapter 3
The Weeping Woman

The bogeyman might get you if you don't watch out. It's just an old wives' tale, right? Well, to millions of Spanish-speaking people, that evil spirit takes the form of La Llorna, the weeping madwoman who roams the streets in search of her lost children. Will she capture you next?

Doña Luisa de Loveros was in love. She had met him when he passed through her village on the outskirts of Mexico City. That first time, their eyes met for just the briefest of moments as he rode by where she lived with her parents and little brothers and sisters. But the next day he was back, and this time he found an excuse to walk the parched road in front of her house. His smile was radiant; his silk and brocaded clothing glistened in the sun. She had never seen anyone that handsome in her life.

She didn't need to be asked. She followed him as eagerly and as mindlessly as if he had been a siren luring a sailor to the shoals.

Luisa discovered that his name was Don Nuno de Montesclaros, and he was a Spanish nobleman who had come to the New World to seek his fortune. Hernando Cortes had conquered the Aztecs just twenty-nine years earlier, so the territory, the don figured, should still be ripe for the picking. With a political appointment and land granted by the crown—he was of the same bloodline as the king—Montesclaros was able to settle quickly into a contented life.

Luisa became his lover the very first night she visited him. Over the next two years, she bore him two babies. You might think that, as his mistress and the mother of his children, she was given some sort of privilege, perhaps a room of her own in the magnificent hacienda. But that was not the case.

True, Montesclaros didn't completely abandon her. He was not a cruel man. He knew he had ruined her and that she could never return home to her village. Still, he had no intention of marrying the girl or acknowledging the children. So he quietly provided a small room in town for them and just enough money for their food and other basic needs. Besides, Montesclaros hadn't grown tired of the girl yet.

Before long, stories began to circulate that Montesclaros had a fiancée, a beautiful señorita who had just arrived from Spain. They had been betrothed since childhood, it turned out, but they had waited until Montesclaros was established in Mexico City to complete their nuptials.

Nuno de Montesclaros held a gala party at his ranch estate to introduce her to all of his new friends—many of whom, to be perfectly honest, were quite envious of his great success, including his good fortune to have a striking, elegant bride in such a backward land as this.

But no one was more jealous than Doña Luisa de Loveros. Why shouldn't *she* be his wife? Hadn't she loved him faithfully, enduring his humiliation, for more than two years? Hadn't she given him two babies?

The subject of marriage had come up between them many times. He always smiled weakly as he sadly explained that it was impossible for them to wed. After all, he was nobility and she was, what? A common—he chose his words carefully so as not to deliberately insult her—a humble native.

No, he was wrong, she pleaded. She was a princess: Her family had told her that she was descended from Aztec royalty. But her words fell on deaf ears. He didn't wish to be malicious or unkind. But facts were facts. It was 1550, and this was Mexico City. He was in the upper class of the conquerors; she was a lowly peasant. A marriage between them could never and would never happen.

The night of the party, Doña Luisa stood outside the Montesclaros hacienda, watching the lights blazing within. She could see the scene in her mind. He was offering a toast: to happiness, to life, to his new bride.

No!

In a fit of insane rage, she knew what she had to do. She knew how to get his attention and her revenge. Luisa calmly returned home. She gently took both of the babies out of their cradles and rocked them in her arms. She gave each one a gentle, final kiss on the forehead. Then she took a small knife, an ornamental dagger that had been a present from the very man who was deserting her . . . and it was over.

As soon as the gruesome task was done, she seemed to wake from a trance. The sight that confronted her was a nightmare. What had she done? In her crazed despair, she smeared the blood over herself and ran out into the street. Her anguished screams soon roused the entire neighborhood. For a week, the madwoman aimlessly roamed the area, first wailing, then murmuring just under her breath about her lost children.

It wasn't long before the *policía* investigated and discovered the murdered infants. For her grisly crime, Doña Luisa de Loveros was sentenced to death. After she was hanged, her body was left to swing from the public gallows for hours as a warning to anyone else who might even contemplate performing such a hideous act.

It wasn't long before her ghost, wearing a long white, bloodstained dress, began to show up on the streets of Mexico City, where she still appears to this day. She cries, "Mis hijos, mis hijos" ("My children, my children"). She grabs at people as they pass by: Do they have her babies? She roams the pathways alongside nearby rivers and creek beds, looking for infants who may have drowned in the rushing water.

But search as she might, La Llorna will never find her children. For La Llorna, the Weeping Woman, will spend eternity searching for the very ones who died at her own hand.

✛

Cudahey was just another depressed factory town by the late 1970s. Most of the people who had settled into that suburb of Gary, Indiana, were Mexican-Americans, drawn to the plentiful jobs in the steel mills. Far from their roots, the close-knit community brought much of their culture with them to the new land. So it was no surprise to anyone when rumors started flying that the ghost of La Llorna had started to appear in town.

But that was a long time ago. As production dwindled in the factories and workers were laid off, sometimes for a few days, sometimes for weeks or months at a time, many of the town's inhabitants moved on, hoping to find more steady employment elsewhere. The old ramshackle wooden homes huddled on the banks of the Calumet River were torn down, and Cudahey was eventually completely swallowed up by Gary and East Chicago. But the Woman in White never disappeared.

Bob was driving north on Cline Avenue, now State Route 912, looking for his client's address. So many of the workshops and warehouses in this area were grouped together down small lanes off the main street that it was pretty easy to miss a particular address if you weren't careful. Half the time the nondescript, gray, flat-roofed units in industrial parks like this had no identification on them at all—no street numbers, no company names, no logos. It's almost as if the owners *wanted* you to get lost.

He wasn't helped by the fact that it was his last meeting on this late October afternoon, and the sun had already begun to set. The structures lining both sides of the road thinned out. Well, that's it, he thought. I missed it. Let me turn around at that next intersection and try again.

As he neared the cloverleaf at West Fifth Avenue (State Highway 20) in what used to be downtown Cudahey, Bob noticed that Cline Avenue was deserted. He crossed the tracks of the Norfolk Southern railroad line and passed under Indiana Toll Road I-90. There in front of him were the dark, shadowy swirls of the dirty Grand Calumet River.

Bob knew the site he was looking for was south of the river. He pulled over to the side of the road to get his bearings. And then he saw her. A tall woman, dressed all in white, her tight-fitting dress tattered at the ends of its sleeves and ripped along the hem at her feet. Long, disheveled, raven-black hair cascaded helter-skelter over her shoulders, almost reaching to her waist. She turned to look at him.

At first, her face was a cipher. It was so pale it seemed to him that there was no face there at all. It must be a trick of the light, Bob thought, what little light was left. He stared at her more closely. Her face *was* pallid, frighteningly so, which would explain his earlier confusion. But sure enough, there were her unmistakable black, long-lashed eyes, ringed by mascara that had bled down both of her ashen cheeks. She had been crying.

Slowly, the almost-luminous figure glided—did she actually float?—to the passenger side of the car. She raised her hand and gently pressed it against the window. My God, thought Bob, those are the longest fingernails I've ever seen! At least two inches long and painted coal-black, the nails had begun to bend downward at the tips of her fingers, curling inward toward her palms.

If he didn't know better, Bob might have thought he was seeing a vampire out of some Gothic horror movie. But such creatures of the night don't really exist. Do they? Bob asked himself as he wound down the window. "May I help you? You seem to be . . . "

She broke him off in mid-sentence. "Yes, please. I'm looking for my two children. They were here, by the river. Before. But by now they must be at the harbor. I have to get there."

Bob was stunned. "Shouldn't we call the police? Or 911? If your children are missing . . ."

"No, everything will be all right. They'll be at the Calumet Harbor. Can you take me there?"

Well, it was out of his way, but she seemed so desperate. Or was she merely crazy? He glanced down at his watch. It was past five. The client he was trying to visit had no doubt already left for the day. He'd make a call later and apologize, then try again first thing in the morning.

"All right. Sure. Get in. It's just a little ways down the road."

The woman eased into the backseat and closed the door gently behind her. To be honest, Bob didn't even hear it open or shut. He looked at her in the rearview mirror, trying to express comfort in his eyes. "Don't worry," he assured her. "We'll be there in just a few minutes."

A few minutes. An instant. Bob didn't know long he had been driving when it happened. But about a half mile down the road, he glanced up into the mirror again and—she had disappeared! She was no longer in the car! But where had she gone? *How* had she gone?

If Bob had mentioned the incident the next day to his client, who had been raised in one of the nearby Hispanic enclaves, he would have discovered that his experience was far from unique. According to legend, the Weeping Woman he met had gone crazy years before in Cudahey and drowned her illegitimate babies in the Calumet River. Now her ghost appears at the intersection of Cline and Fifth or on the overpass to the harbor looking for her children.

But Bob didn't ask. He never learned the identity of the mysterious stranger he had encountered the night before. And he was never aware that he had had a brief, personal brush with the Unknown, courtesy of the bewitching La Llorna.

Chapter 4
The Prophecy

You're out with friends, minding your own business, when a stranger intrudes. What do you do if that uninvited guest begins to predict the future? Especially if ignoring the prophecy could result in your death? And if that spectral visitor is from the Church? Three young men had to face these questions and more when they picked up the wrong hitchhiker in the shadow of a volcano.

"What's black and white and black and white and black and white all over?"

"I don't know, Christopher, what?"

"A nun rolling down a hill."

"Wait! I got one!" Francis chimed in. "What do you call a nun that walks in her sleep? A Roamin' Catholic!"

"Now, that's just stupid!"

"And yours wasn't?"

"Come on, guys," broke in Anthony. "Enough with the nun jokes, or we're all gonna go to . . . well, you know where."

"Where? Mother Superior's office—again? Oh, no! Not the ruler!"

"No," Anthony warned, pointing a finger straight down. "Someplace a little lower."

The three students knew they were alone in the car, but maybe God was listening. Better to be safe than sorry. They cut out the jokes.

As they drove silently on I-5 from Eugene, Oregon, to Tacoma, Washington, the huge mountain loomed off to their right in the distance. Although they had always lived beside the volcano, the boys had never given it much thought. There hadn't been a major rumble from Mount St. Helens since they were born.

The boys had studied the volcano in school. People were living on its slopes, located in the Cascades Mountains Range, at least 6,500 years ago. Around 1,500 B.C. a major eruption buried anyone and anything in the area under a deep deposit of pumice. For two millennia, Native Americans had avoided the volcano, but by the time the Lewis and Clark expedition reached the Pacific in 1805, the Yakama, Upper Chinook, Klickitat, Taidnapam, and Cowlitz tribes had been settling its foothills for about a thousand years.

Although the famous explorers saw the volcano as they floated downstream on the Columbia River, they didn't witness any activity. But Mount St. Helens had erupted only five to ten years earlier. Over the next sixty years, there would be occasional seismic tremors, as well as the so-called Great Eruption of 1842.

But now everyone was safe. It was the early spring of 1980. Although smoke plumes were seen from time to time— in fact, there was one now—the volcano had last exploded in 1854.

Francis, the history buff, knew lots of ancient legends that explained the formation and eruptions at Mount St. Helens. His favorite came from the Klickitat tribe. Their chief god, Tyhee Saghalie, and his two sons, Klickitat (or Paho) and Wy'east, came from the far north to settle at the narrows of the Columbia near the present-day city of The Dalles, Oregon. (What was it about The Dalles that attracted settlers? thought Francis. It had also been the end of the land journey of the Oregon Trail.)

In any case, in the volcano creation myth, the sons began to fight for possession of the land. To separate them, their father shot two arrows in opposite directions and told his sons to each follow one and settle where the arrow fell. He built a passage, the Bridge of the Gods, between them.

But that didn't end the family squabbles. Both sons fell in love with a young woman named Loowit, and their violent fights over her devastated the earth, causing earthquakes, leveling forests, and destroying the sky bridge, which tumbled to the ground to form the Cascades.

Finally, to put an end to the destruction, Saghalie turned all three of the others into stone. His son Klickitat became what today is called Mount Adams. To the south, his brother Wy'est became Mount Hood. And beautiful Loowit was transformed into Mount St. Helens, which was called Louwala-Clough (or "smoking fire mountain") by the Klickitat.

The guys checked out the peak of the mountain. A little smoke trail today, but nothing to be worried about. Besides, there were scientists up there now, apparently, checking it out. Wouldn't they tell people if it were going to blow?

"Holy Mother of Jesus. Speak of the devil!"

Christopher motioned up ahead. About fifty yards down the highway, standing alone on the shoulder of the road, was a woman. She looked to be about fifty or sixty years old. She was in a black dress, a white collar, and a black and white wimple. The look was unmistakable. She was a nun.

As they watched, the sister smiled gently and then, at the last second, almost comically stuck a curved thumb up into the air. She was hitchhiking!

A hitchhiking nun! Now they'd seen everything!

"Well, do you think we should pick her up?"

"You have to, dude. She's a nun. Isn't there some kind of rule that we have to stop to help her out?"

"Do you think she's really a nun?"

"Do you think we can risk it if she's not? What if we leave her standing there, and then, I don't know, someone finds out . . ."

"I told you we shouldn't have been telling those jokes!"

"All right, everybody take a deep breath," Christopher warned as he slowed the car. "Best behavior. We're going in."

A slight pause, and then all three burst out laughing.

"A *Star Wars* quote? Nice touch, Chris. How about this one: 'I have a very bad feeling about this'?"

"Luke! Use the force!"

They were still chuckling as the car came to a halt. Polite to a fault, all three boys stepped out of the car. Francis spoke up first. "May we offer you a ride, sister? We're only going a few miles up the road, just to Tacoma."

When she spoke, they were surprised to hear such a soft voice, not stern like their teachers at school. "Tacoma would be fine. Thank you."

Francis, realizing that he had been riding shotgun, opened the front passenger door for the sister. Once she was inside, he closed the door carefully and hopped in the back with Anthony.

"Where are you boys heading? To Bellarmine Preparatory?"

Bellarmine? the three guys thought. Although that *didn't* happen to be where they were headed, they knew the school well. Bellarmine, in Tacoma, was one of the leading Catholic prep schools in the whole area. How can she know, just by looking at them, that they were Catholic? Were nuns psychic, too?

The sister couldn't help but notice the quizzical expression on their faces. With a twinkle in her eye, she explained.

"Forgive me if I'm wrong—and I doubt if I am—but I knew you must be Catholic. You were so well-mannered when you stopped to assist me that I just assumed you've been raised in Catholic schools."

Her voice was smooth, liquid, calming. Why couldn't she be teaching one of their classes? That voice made you want to listen to her all day.

Before long, she was sharing her story, what had brought her to that spot on the road where they had first spied her. She was on a mission, she said, a sort of assignment she had been instructed—she didn't say by whom—to perform. She was to meet strangers, people in need of help.

But then her tone darkened. Yes, she said, it was like the story in the Old Testament of the young men who appeared at Lot's gate. If her message was well-received, goodness would come to the people who heard her words, but if she was met with disbelief or hostility, the offenders would surely suffer the wrath of the Lord.

The boys squirmed in their car seats. This was not what they wanted to hear. They were just out having fun. But they couldn't ask a nun to "hold off on the preaching," could they? Was this a test? Was God watching them? Anthony involuntarily looked up.

Her voice, once like honey, now was becoming stern and menacing. But they couldn't resist hanging on her words.

"As Jesus said in the Book of St. Matthew, 'If anyone will not welcome you or listen to your words, shake the dust off your feet when you leave that home or town. I tell you the truth, it will be more bearable for Sodom and Gomorrah on the day of judgment than for that town.'"

Now the guys were freaked. What was she trying to tell them? They stared into her face, but it was no longer gentle and loving. It had become transfixed, severe. The voice had become enraptured, messianic, and her whole manner had become detached, as if she were possessed.

Suddenly it occurred to the boys: She was no longer directly addressing them. She was delivering prophecy.

The nun turned her unfathomable face toward the side window. She stared up at the dome of Mount St. Helens. "For I tell you this: The time approaches. Those who do not seek forgiveness for their transgressions and do not change the errors of their ways, they will be consumed by fire and ash."

The clouds parted, and as the last rays of sun burst upon the side of the towering mountain, it became crystal clear. She was telling them the volcano was going to erupt—and soon! If they weren't penitent or didn't seek absolution (were those the right words?), they would die in the explosion.

Then the most incredible thing the boys had ever experienced—and, indeed, ever would experience—happened. The nun began to glow and then, with a small pop, vanished.

Startled, Christopher involuntarily slammed on the brakes and veered onto the side of the road. Had that really just happened? Where was she? How could she have just disappeared?

But, clearly, the miracle had taken place. The front passenger seat screamed its emptiness.

Struck dumb, the young men continued on to Tacoma without saying a word. The boys never told anyone about their ethereal visitor. If they had, who would have believed them? Besides, they had enough demerits at school; they certainly weren't going to start telling stories about a doomsday nun. Everyone would dismiss it as a tasteless prank or, worse, a drug-induced hallucination.

If the boys had checked in with the Tacoma police, however, they would have found they were not alone. Over the past few years, more than twenty reports had come in from individuals as well as carloads of people that had experienced exactly the same thing. They had all stopped to pick up a middle-aged woman, usually but not always dressed in a nun's habit, who warned the motorists that if they didn't repent their sins, they would die in an accident on the highway. In the last couple of months, she had changed her apocalyptic story to center on Mount St. Helens.

As it turned out, the nun was right. At least in part.

On May 18, 1980, after several months of underground murmurs, Mount St. Helens exploded. The north side of the mountain blew out, causing a debris avalanche that stripped away everything in its path. Plumes of pumice and steam followed, covering miles around with a layer of ash. Fifty-seven people were killed, and two hundred fifty houses were destroyed. Miles of road and railway were wiped out, as were forty-seven bridges. By far, it was the deadliest and costliest volcanic eruption in U.S. history.

Had the mysterious sister accurately predicted the desolation? Was she describing Mount St. Helens's eruption to her captive audiences at all, or was she really trying to relay a holy vision of the Judgment Day? In fact, had she even been real, an angel of the Lord? Or had the boys actually seen a ghost?

Part Two

STREET WALKERS

You never know whom you might bump into walking down the street. Even a well-traveled hiking trail, an innocent-looking garden path, or a rustic bridge might be home to some restless spirit.

In the next few chapters you'll meet some amazing characters: From Hawaii, the Night Marcher warriors and the fire goddess Pele make an appearance; from Japan, Oiwa, the ghost of a murdered bride; and from the American South, abolitionist John Brown and plantation owner William Baynard. For good measure, you'll also find a haunted bridge and a spectral nun that glides along a garden trail. So if you see *them* as you stroll down the street, walk on by.

Chapter 5

Madame Pele
Pays a Visit

Do spirits of the gods walk among us? And if so, why do they inter-act with us mere mortals? One such deity, Madame Pele, is kind enough to drop by to warn us before her volcanic outbursts. Other times her appearances are mere mischief or simply augur misfor-tune. But one thing's certain: She's here, and she's not going away.

The mysterious woman in the flowing red muumuu accompa-nied by a small white dog at her side was being seen again at night along the lonely, deserted roads all over the Big Island of Hawaii. When would the next eruption begin? It was a question locals had been asking for generations, and the answer always led back to the beginning of time.

There was trouble in Paradise. Pele, the daughter of Kane-hoa-lani and the goddess Haumea, was born in Kahiki. (That's Tahiti to you and me.) She had a huge family, and all of her brothers and sisters were gods or goddesses over dif-ferent aspects of the natural world. Pele's specialty was fire, especially in the way it frequently showed itself throughout the Polynesian world: She possessed the power to produce the flames and molten lava of the volcano.

But just like in many large human families, there were constant quarrels and bickering among the brothers and sis-ters. In the case of Pele, the thorn in her side was her sis-ter Na-maka-o-ka-ha'i, who was a goddess of the sea. Now, let's be honest: It was probably Pele's fault. Pele had—how should we say this delicately?—great womanly needs, and her power to transform into any human form or age greatly helped her in her conquests. By changing herself into a young, sensuous woman, she was able to attract any man she desired.

Unfortunately, one of those men, it's said, was the husband of her sister Na-maka-o-ka-ha'i. Furious at Pele and jealous of her great beauty, Na-maka-o-ka-ha'i would force the waves of the sea over the coastline and up into the foothills wherever Pele settled, snuffing out her flames. After centuries of torment, Pele decided to leave Kahiki and find a new home in the great islands to the northeast.

She pleaded her case to her father and, once granted permission to depart, Pele formed a gigantic canoe to cross the oceans. She wasn't going to travel alone, of course. Several of her relatives decided to go with her, as did forty thousand lesser deities. To find their new home, Pele asked her brother Ka-mo'o-ali'i, who had a shark body, to swim in front of the boat to guide her. Even so, the journey was marked with difficulties: Ever resentful, Na-maka-o-ka-ha'i tossed wave after wave at the vessel, trying to sink the craft.

Eventually, Pele arrived at the chain of islands we call Hawaii, stopping first at the tiny outcrop of Niihau, then onto Kauai, followed by Oahu. At every turn, when Pele tried to create a new home for herself deep in the rock by using her magic digging stick, Na-maka-o-ka-ha'i would fill the hole with water, either by having it seep up through the ground or by tossing tidal waves up from the coast.

The monumental battle between the sisters came to a head on the island of Maui, where Pele settled into the crater Haleakala. Fire and water nearly consumed each other in the clash between the titans, and in the end Pele was snuffed out and consumed. To this day, her bones can be seen on the road to Hana in the form of a huge cinder cone called Ka Iwi o Pele.

Content in her victory, Na-maka-o-ka-ha'i returned to Kahiki. But Pele lived on in spirit form. She moved to the Big Island of Hawaii, where she was finally able to dig a pit deep enough and far enough inland that it was out of her sister's reach. Today that home is the 13,680-foot volcano known as Mauna Loa.

But Pele still roamed the earth looking for consorts. According to tradition, she traveled as a spirit from her home on Hawaii to the island of Kauai, where she happened upon Lohiau, a handsome human chieftain. She made the mistake of asking her youngest sister, Hi'iaka-i-ka-poli-o-Pele, to bring the warrior back to her on the Big Island, but during the trip Hi'iaka fell in love with the chief herself. In a fit of jealous rage, Pele killed the chieftain—twice—but both times Hi'iaka brought him back to life.

Pele's greatest romantic battle was with Kamapua'ua, a shape-shifting deity who usually appeared as a pig or, when in human form, with a bristly, boarlike back. Pele found herself the object of his unwanted affection. The volcano goddess rejected Kamapua'ua, but that only seemed to spur him on. Every time he tried to approach Pele, she held him back with her fire. Kamapua'ua would then call on his sister to cover Pele with fog and torrents of rain. The colossal war raged for ages, until finally Pele's fires had diminished to the point that she was almost extinguished. Eventually, Pele conceded defeat. The gods made love, and Pele's flames were restored. (As a final insult to Pele, after she bore him a child, Kamapua'ua deserted her, leaving her alone in her fiery abyss.)

Today a ridge road, Crater Rim Drive, surrounds the great Kilauea Caldera on the eastern slope of Mauna Loa on Hawaii. For years drivers along the path have reported seeing a woman, usually young but sometimes elderly, walking on the shoulder of the road. It's Pele, in human form, walking the earth! If she's wearing white, the motorist or someone he or she knows is going to fall ill. But if Pele's wearing red, it usually means a volcanic eruption will take place within days!

Madame Pele has never sat quietly in her home at the bottom of the 280-foot deep Halema'umau'au Crater in the Kilauea Caldera. She would frequently become angry if the mortals living on her island didn't worship her or leave her tributes, and in her blazing temper she would start a flow of lava or shoot sparks and flames high into the air. To this day, locals will try to appease her by laying offerings of chicken or alcohol along the rim of the crater.

Also according to legend, if you remove any piece of lava from the islands, Pele will curse you. Bad luck will follow you until you return the stones to their native shores.

All quaint stories? Just ancient myths of gods and goddesses? Maybe. And yet the appearances of Madame Pele's ghost on the Hawaiian Islands occur quite frequently, and the sightings are far too numerous to dismiss as the products of mere imagination.

If you're driving anywhere on the island in the middle of the night and you see a young, attractive woman in a red muumuu on the side of the road, it's best that you stop to offer Madame Pele a ride. Don't worry: Almost as soon as she steps inside your car, she will disappear from sight. But if you don't invite her in, you'll undoubtedly anger her, which will result in your own death or set off a new round of volcanic eruptions and devastation to the island.

She still gives her forewarnings. Residents of Kapoho swear that in 1960 Madame Pele showed up two days before the 2,600-foot-wide lava flow from Mauna Loa destroyed their town. In fact, many old tales surround the volcanic eruptions that have affected the Kapoho region. In one of the best known, a local chieftain challenged a young lady to race him by sled down the mountainside. He was halfway down the slope when he looked beside him to discover that the woman was actually Madame Pele, and she was riding a river of lava.

And apparently Pele is still on the prowl for companions. In recent years, the spectre of a striking lady in the trademark flaming red muumuu has been seen roaming the halls of the hotel towers in the Hilton Hawaiian Village in Honolulu, Hawaii. Now, some people think she's the phantom of a woman who was murdered in the hotel, but most locals agree that she's most likely the ghostly manifestation of Pele herself. She certainly isn't warning the visitors about volcanoes, though. Is it possible she's looking for a new lover? If you're in Hawaii on vacation, be careful whom you meet in your hotel hallway. It could be Madame Pele paying a visit.

Chapter 6
The Night Marchers

The folklore of Hawaii is filled with stories of spirit orbs, legends of the mysterious Menehune, or "Little People," and tales of ghosts and apparitions. But none is more amazing than that of the Night Marchers, the parade of spirit warriors that pass over the old trails that crisscross the islands. Just seeing the procession can mean death—unless you're lucky enough to have someone, or something, intervene.

Cutting across the grassy plain of the Nuuanu Valley, Kaimi knew he was late. Where had the time gone? It was already after sundown, and even though streaks of red still lit the western sky, he had promised his mother he would be home hours before this.

Not that he was too young to be out on his own. Heck, he was almost eighteen. But, as his mom had often warned him, "You can't be too careful these days. You never know who you'll run into. Or who will run into you."

Kaimi's mother meant that both figuratively and literally because, these days, drivers seemed to be zooming across the island at top speed. If they're unfamiliar with the roads—and this was the height of tourist season—they could very easily drift just a little too much toward the shoulder and hit someone innocently walking down the side of the highway.

Which is one of the reasons Kaimi was now taking the hiking trail toward his home. Walking along the cliffs, Kaimi always felt most in touch with his native Hawaiian roots—

something his grandfather Maleko had instilled in him when he was just a little boy.

Maleko knew the traditions well. He had still been a young man when businessmen, led by politician Sanford Dole (a cousin of James Dole, the pineapple magnate), overthrew Queen Liliuokalani in 1893. The queen, hoping to spare her subjects from bloodshed, asked them to be patient while she petitioned Washington, D.C., for the return of her throne, but many natives revolted against the new government. The rebellion was squashed, but to his dying day Maleko was proud that he had joined in the struggle.

Liliuokalani was allowed to leave house arrest in the Iolani Palace in Honolulu in 1896, but there was no turning back for the islands. The monarchy had been dissolved forever. Over the years, as mainland people moved to Hawaii, more and more of the natives abandoned their old ways.

But Maleko resisted. As he raised his children he made sure that they learned the language and all the ancient legends of his people. Then, as they had children of their own, Maleko insisted that they be taught the native customs as well.

Now Maleko was gone, but Kaimi treasured the memory of the many lessons he had learned at his grandfather's knee. That was one of the reasons he loved to walk in the Nuuanu Pali. Not only could he catch a panoramic view all the way from the top of the mountains down to the windward beaches of Oahu, but he also knew the area was steeped in Hawaiian history. In fact, the bloodiest battle in the fight for Hawaiian unification took place very close to where he was standing.

In 1795, Kamehameha I (known as King Kamehameha the Great) and ten thousand of his warriors sailed from his base on the island of Hawaii to conquer first Maui and then Molokai before moving here to Oahu. In the fierce Battle of Nuuanu, Kamehameha drove the chieftain Kalanikupule and his men across the valley floor, where Kaimi had been earlier that day, up onto the top of the perilous cliff. At the climax of the monumental clash, hundreds of Kalanikupule's warriors were forced over the precipice. In the aftermath, Kamehameha was able to bring all of the Hawaiian Islands under his rule.

Kaimi fell in step on the Old Pali Highway. The first road over the Nuuanu Pali connecting the windward towns of Kandohe and Kailua with Honolulu was constructed in 1845. When the road was upgraded in 1898, more than eight hundred skulls, no doubt from the warriors who had plummeted to their deaths a hundred years earlier, were uncovered. In the 1950s, the Old Pali Highway was replaced by a new road with tunnels cut through the mountains. About three miles of the old highway still existed, however. Much of the way was now overshadowed by bending trees that bordered its length, and hikers like Kaimi often walked along the paved road, the meandering Nuuanu Pali Drive nearby, and the hillside trails surrounding them.

Of all the tales his grandfather had told Kaimi, he liked the ghost stories best. Maleko had warned him to always be on guard when he walked through this area, because Nuuanu Pali was said to be haunted.

"What do you mean? Do you see spirits there?"

"Sometimes, Kaimi, sometimes. A man named Morgan Wilder had his home up there on the Old Pali road. He died back in 1948, killed himself, but it's not *his* ghost that haunts the highway. It's a little girl who hanged herself on a tree at the hairpin turn known as Morgan's Creek near where he lived on Nuuanu Pali Drive. By the time they found the girl a few days later, her head had separated from the body. Her corpse was put back together and buried, but as you go by that withered old tree you can make out a mysterious black shape up among the leaves. Sometimes you can even see her ghost hanging from one of its limbs! And if you're not careful, she might jump out at you."

There were other Oahu ghost stories, and Kaimi loved them all. For instance, they say that if you walk alone out in the fields or woodlands at night without a flashlight, you'll be attacked by a phantom woman dressed in white. Most often she just scares you, but some people claim that if you get too close to her, she'll kill you.

Then, if you drive past the cemetery across from the Kahala Mall with your windows open, an invisible spirit will jump into your car with you. Even though you can't see it, you can feel its presence sitting in the backseat, right behind you. Sometimes you can actually make out the phantom: it's the ghost of a little girl. But as you drive away from the cemetery, the spectral presence evaporates.

Perhaps the strangest legend claims that you should never carry pork in your car if you're driving over State Route 61, the new Pali Highway. (This was true for the original Pali road when it was the main passageway over the mountains as well.) If you do, your car will stall or break down somewhere along the road, usually stranding you in a dark, deserted area, until the meat is removed from your car.

In one retelling of the story, a taxi driver crossing the Nuuanu Pali was grabbed from behind by an invisible force as she passed through one of the tunnels. The unseen spectre pushed her body and head into the steering wheel, almost causing her to crash, but it let go as soon as the driver exited the tunnel. When she later cleaned out her car, she found a half-eaten pork sandwich left in the car by a passenger.

In Kaimi's favorite version of the tale, if the spirits stop your car on the highway because you're carrying pork, a phantom white dog will appear next to your car. All you have to do to get your car running again is crack your window and drop out the forbidden meat. As soon as the dog has eaten it, the canine will vanish and, at the same moment, your car engine will start up.

Kaimi loved to strike out on his own to investigate all these old ghost stories. According to Hawaiian tradition, his name meant "seeker," and he knew that people who have the name are said to be able to uncover secrets and hidden truths. Indeed, Kaimi never took what people said at face value. He had to examine what he was told, to make sure for himself before he was able to believe. Yes, "Kaimi" fit him like a glove. How could his parents have known when he was only a few days old that it would be the perfect name for him? Had Grandfather Maleko, who knew such things, told them?

Now it was dark. There were no houses in sight, and as he left the Old Pali Highway far behind, there was little light. It was hard to make out the trail. Kaimi knew he had to be careful.

At first he thought he was imagining it. But then, rising over the whisper of the grass, he could make out the faint sound of men's voices. Singing. Chanting. Steady. Soft, but intense. They were accompanied by the rhythm of drums and an *ohe hano ihu*, the bamboo nose flute. The voices seemed to be coming from just over the next ridge, up ahead. They got stronger. The men must have been getting closer.

As Kaimi reached the top of the hill, he saw the flickering. Not from flashlights or distant traffic, but from fire. He could make out dozens of separate flames coming from the ends of handheld torches. The shadowy figures carrying them were walking four or six across, drawing toward him on the earthen path.

Kaimi stopped abruptly, puzzled. Who would be out here in the desolate fields in the dark, carrying torches, chanting? And then it struck him: They were Night Marchers!

The Night Marchers, the *huaka'i o ka po,* as they were known in Hawaiian, were ghosts of venerated warriors, chiefs, or even deities that roamed the earth. Although they could materialize anytime, they most often appeared between 7:30 p.m. and dawn on one of the special nights at the end of the month on the Hawaiian calendar that was dedicated to the native gods.

As they traveled from ancient battlefields, the Marchers collected the souls of dead chieftains and warriors, as well as their descendants, both male and female. As they passed, spirits of the dead who were worthy would join their ranks. Then the entire parade would move on, heading either toward the nearest *heiau* (or temple), one of the outcroppings or beach promontories that acted as a jumping-off point to the Next World, or some other sacred spot.

Kaimi had thought the Night Marchers were only a myth, like all the other ghost stories. But now, here, one of those "myths" had come to life and was about to meet him face-to-face.

He tried desperately to remember everything his grandfather had told him about the Night Marchers. He knew an encounter with them could be deadly. In fact, they *usually* were. Over the years, police had found the bodies of people lying on the ground, face-up, their eyes and mouths wide open, their arms frozen in place in front of them as if they had died trying to fight off assailants. But there were never any marks on the corpses, no signs of assault. Medical examiners always decided that the victims had died of heart attacks, but native Hawaiians, raised on tales of the fearsome Night Marchers, knew what had really happened.

Kaimi's mind raced. What was he supposed to do to survive?

That's right! First of all, don't look any of them in the eye. Don't try to run; you don't want to catch their attention if they haven't seen you yet. Quickly judge which way they're heading and get out of their way. Then stop, and drop to the ground.

The warriors seemed to be following the old dirt footpath that had been worn into the hillside long before the Old Pali Highway was made. Kaimi got off the trail and moved swiftly about twenty feet to one side. If the men didn't spread out too wide and he was lucky, they might miss him.

Kaimi got down. He lay there, panting, terrified, as the phantoms grew closer and closer. He knew that, even lying flat on the ground, he wasn't safe. He was supposed to do something else. What was it?

He let his mind drift back. Tell me, Grandfather, he whispered to himself. Tell me, what am I to do? Then, as if in a dream, he could see himself as a young boy. There he was, six years old, sitting by his grandfather, and the old man was talking about the dreaded Night Marchers.

"Some of the elders say that when you see them you are to lie on the ground with your eyes closed, say nothing, and breathe as little as possible until long after the spirits have passed by. Some say that it helps if you take off all of your clothing and lay face upward."

"But why would I do that, *kupunakane*? They would see . . . everything."

"Yes, that is the point, my little *mo'opuna*. But that is what may save you. As the warriors and the chief's guards pass you by, they will see you there, undressed, and cry, 'Shame. Shame on you for being uncovered.' They will feel you have dishonored yourself and your ancestors, so they will leave you behind without stopping. There is no guarantee that it will work. But it may make the difference that could save your life."

Without a thought, Kaimi ripped off his shirt. Soon he was down to his underwear—even in the legends, you only had to strip to your loincloth—when he realized that it was too late. They were upon him. He kept his head down. He didn't dare look directly at them. It would mean instant death. But Kaimi couldn't resist taking a peek. He lifted his eyes just as two warriors raised their spears.

"Strike him!"

"No, stop! He is mine!"

From behind the guards, a third warrior stepped forward. "The boy is my flesh and my blood, of my family. You will not harm him." He pushed past the spectres that were just about to kill Kaimi, turned toward them, and planted his feet in front of the boy, shielding him. The two guards hesitated for only a moment, then moved back to join the procession.

Kaimi sat there—how long?—five minutes? A half hour? The glimmer of torchlight disappeared as the ranks of the Night Marchers moved over the next ridge. The sounds of their chanting, the drums, the flutes, faded in the wind.

Still, the lone guardian stood over him. Kaimi didn't move. Then he remembered: Only an *aumakua,* the spirit of some ancestor that marched with the phantom warriors, could protect you once they had turned against you. Who was his savior?

The warrior looked down to face the boy, who was now shivering, nearly naked, under the moonlit sky.

"You may open your eyes, my grandson. You learned well. You are safe."

Kaimi stared up at the spirit hovering over him. The warrior was young, powerful, handsome. The passage into the Other World had changed his appearance, back to a time long before Kaimi had been born, yet the man was unmistakable. The protector standing before him was his grandfather Maleko.

Of course! Maleko. His grandfather's name was Hawaiian for "warlike." His grandfather, who had chosen to take part in the native uprising all those years ago, was descended from warriors! No wonder he was now one of the Night Marchers.

Kaimi was going to live! He had never felt such love for his grandfather.

"Yes, you are safe now, my foolish, reckless grandson. I could not let them hurt you. One day, if you wish, you may join us, for you, too, come from a long line of warriors. But for now, my little Kaimi, aloha." And with that, the apparition dissolved. He had gone to join his fellow Night Marchers.

Mahalo, Grandfather, thought Kaimi. Thank you. *Mahalo nui loa.*

Chapter 7
Oiwa's Ghost

A terrifying creature roams the streets of Tokyo at night. And it's not Godzilla. It's Oiwa, the sinister ghost of a betrayed wife who seeks retribution for her mutilation and murder hundreds of years in the past. Beware, or you might become her next victim.

She was the most beautiful woman Shigeo had ever seen. Not that he caught a very good look of her, mind you. He noticed her as he was coming out of Shibuya Station, her long black hair framing a delicate face. She paused briefly to look at the statue of Hachiko, the loyal dog that had stood by the station faithfully for seven years, waiting for a dead master who would never come.

She continued on. Shigeo, who had come downtown for a few casual hours of idle people-watching, suddenly put those ideas on hold. He decided to follow the mysterious stranger. Was this what, in America, they call stalking?

As he walked down the district's jammed nighttime streets, he occasionally caught a glimpse of the woman as she slipped in and out among the throngs of shoppers and clubgoers. The petite woman seemed to positively glow. Dressed in a long, elegant white kimono, tied at the waist with a wide, faintly colored *obi,* the enchantress seemed to be dressed for a celebration. Sure, kimonos were still common here on the streets of Tokyo, and Shigeo saw them every day. But among the young they usually were reserved for special occasions.

There she was again! She must have briefly darted down a side street, but now she was on Koen Dori heading . . . where?

She was moving away from all the major hotels. Surely if she were dressed to attend a private party she would head to one of the dozens of function rooms in Center Gai.

Propelled by curiosity alone—quite uncharacteristic for Shigeo—he hastened his step. The crowds had thinned out. She had stopped, standing on her own, separate from any passersby, and looked neither left nor right. It was almost as if she were waiting. For him?

Shigeo came up close behind her. Dare he? He reached out a hand and touched her lightly on her left shoulder. "*Sumi-masen.*" I'm sorry, he said, please excuse me.

Suddenly the maiden's right arm thrust upward, and she clamped her palm on top of his hand. He stared at her flesh. It was bloodless, almost blue, and ice cold. She spun to face him, and involuntarily Shigeo let out a shriek.

She was no longer the flawless beauty he had seen just minutes before. She had somehow transformed into an old hag, a ghoul, with a disfigured, weathered face and red, burning eyes that stared at him maliciously. Her right eye drooped frighteningly, as if all the muscles around it had died and fallen slack. Her hair, which had seemed so lustrous, was now stringy and disheveled, and bald patches clearly showed through. Parting her thin, pasty lips, she revealed rotting, jagged teeth. Were they fangs?

Shigeo's eyes dropped to her kimono, and to his horror he realized the wide garment was bound up the wrong way. The silken cloth was wrapped around her right to left, in the form of a burial kimono. Why, that meant the woman standing before him was no longer living. She must be a ghost!

Shigeo snatched back his hand. Had touching this demon sealed his doom? The creature smiled wickedly. She seemed to be feeding, growing stronger, on his fear. A low, guttural cackle emerged from her throat. She pressed her right hand over her heart—or where her heart would have been if she were alive—then reached out and pointed her left forefinger at his chest. The gesture was unmistakable: She loved him.

Of course! Shigeo suddenly realized why the hellish being was in a formal kimono. The succubus was dressed as a bride. The ghost must have been spurned by her husband, and she was now out for revenge! Was he was about to become her victim? Or had she chosen him as her new consort?

Shigeo stepped back. Odd. She didn't follow. He moved again. Still, she stood anchored to the spot. As he watched, the fire in her eyes dimmed, leaving them blank, soulless. Then her whole body seemed to fade. There was a flicker, and the banshee was gone.

A door from one of the clubs burst open, and people began to spill out onto the sidewalk. Had their arrival scared the evil spirit away? Whatever the reason, he was thankful he was no longer alone with the demon. His energy drained and emotions spent, Shigeo breathed a sigh of relief. He would not be Oiwa's next victim after all.

⚜

Iemon, once a respected samurai during the feudal wars, had lost favor with his master and was forced to become one of the ronin who drifted from lord to lord as their services were required. Of course, according to the *Bushido Shoshinshu*, or Code of the Samurai, he was supposed to have committed *oibara seppuku*, or, as some more sordidly referred to it, *hara kiri*. But he had chosen not to perform ritual suicide, and the defiant act brought even more shame to him and his family.

Yes, family, because Iemon was married. During his courtship of the lovely Oiwa, the girl's father had found out about the awful deeds that had led to Iemon's dismissal, and to prevent the old man from exposing his secrets and calling off the wedding, Iemon secretly killed him.

Without employment and shunned by his fellow samurai, Iemon was forced to take up a lowly trade, making umbrellas, to sustain his wife and baby. Slowly, imperceptibly, he began to resent Oiwa, blaming her for his poverty and disgrace. He had no cause, of course, but that didn't matter to a man who was slowly starting to go mad.

Then, out of the blue, Iemon's new neighbor, who knew nothing about the samurai's past, offered him a way out. He was rich, and if only Iemon would desert Oiwa and marry his attractive granddaughter, he would support the former warrior to the end of his days. Iemon immediately consented, but he suggested a dark twist: Why not kill Oiwa to clear the way completely? That way no dishonor would follow him for leaving Oiwa behind.

A murder scheme was devised. Oiwa had become sick following the birth of her baby, and she was still quite weak. Iemon concocted a poison, which he gave her as medicine, promising it would restore her health and vitality.

Oiwa, trusting and naive, took the potion. But to Iemon's dismay it did not kill her. Instead, it paralyzed the right side of her body and her face, causing one cheek to sag. Her hair started to fall out in clumps, and her face was so ravaged that it turned the once-stunning Oiwa into a hideous crone. When she finally had the strength to leave her bed to look into a mirror, the shock of seeing the gorgon she had become, coupled with the dawning awareness that it was her husband who had done this to her, caused her frail heart to stop.

But the tragedy had only begun. Kobote Kohei, a devoted household servant, discovered what Iemon had done. To stop him from telling anyone, the ronin accused Kohei of theft and had the innocent man executed. In a gruesome act of insane desecration, Iemon nailed the bodies of Oiwa and Kohei to opposite sides of a wooden door and threw it into the furious rapids of a river.

Seemingly with no other obstacles to his plan, Iemon married his patron's granddaughter. Alone with his bride after the wedding ceremony, he lifted her veil only to see— how could it be?—the face of his dead wife, Oiwa, glaring at him accusingly. Bedecked for the festivities in his full samurai attire, the terrified warrior drew one of the swords from his waist and, in a single slice, chopped off Oiwa's head.

Instantly his mind and eyes cleared, as if he were emerging from a fog. He looked down to the lifeless body. The face staring back at him from the severed head was not the repulsive Oiwa but that of his new bride.

Shaken, Iemon ran to his neighbor to tell him the dreadful news, but when he entered the house, he found Kohei's ghost waiting for him instead. Iemon lifted his other sword and hacked at the phantom. Only when he heard the heavy thud of a very real, corporeal body hitting the floor did he comprehend what he had actually done: He had murdered his neighbor, the father of the woman he had just married, the woman he had just killed.

Pursued by Oiwa's merciless spirit, Iemon fled into the hills. Oiwa haunted him day and night, without end. Her face appeared on the shades of the lanterns in his room; billowing smoke changed into strands of her hair. Finally, while fishing in the river, his line snagged the door that still held the corpses of Oiwa and Kohei. Deranged, Iemon ran from the mountainside screaming. On the path, he was met by Oiwa's brother, who was coming to avenge her. In the short struggle that ensued, Iemon, exhausted and ready for release from torment, was killed.

Some claim Oiwa is now buried at a temple named Myogo-ji, which is located in Yotsuya, in the Shinjuku district of Tokyo. On the marker, the date of her death is given as February 22, 1636. Is this the same Oiwa?

Regardless, according to legend, her spirit has never felt that justice was served. In the many versions of the ancient tale, Oiwa is an *onryo*, a ghost that returns to earth to seek revenge. Her apparition still appears throughout Japan to this day, and her spectre is often seen on the busy streets of modern Tokyo. Even people not familiar with her ancient tale of sorrow fall prey, people like unsuspecting Shigeo. And who will be her next target? Could it be you?

Chapter 8

The Funeral Cortege of Baynard Plantation

There are stories of phantom stagecoaches and wagons galore, but the sighting of a spectral horse-drawn funeral carriage is a rare sight indeed. For more than a hundred years, that's what some local residents of one South Carolina seaside resort have claimed to have seen. And it turns out to be more than just a trip to the grave: It's also a search for a missing cadaver.

Today, Hilton Head Island is a dream vacation getaway. Located in South Carolina along the Georgia border, the Atlantic Ocean retreat is just twenty miles outside of Savannah. With all the multimillion-dollar resorts, twelve miles of snow-white sand, and more than two dozen premier golf courses—Hilton Head is a stop on the PGA tour—it's hard to believe the first bridge onto the island opening it to automobile traffic wasn't constructed until 1956.

But the story of the Baynard Plantation ghost dates back much further, to a simpler time, when cotton was king and the island found itself trapped in the struggle between Union forces and the Confederacy during the War Between the States.

Spanish explorers led by Francisco Gordillo were the first Europeans to make contact with the natives living on the island in 1521. By the 1600s the land had become English territory, and in 1663 Charles II granted a wide swath of land in the Americas to eight men known as the Lord Proprietors. That same year, Captain William Hilton sailed from Barbados on the *Adventure* and visited the region on their behalf. Off the coast of the Carolinas, he gave his name to this particularly attractive small islet located at the "head" of Port Royal Sound.

In 1776 a sea captain named John Stoney bought a thousand acres known as Braddock's Point (named for Captain David Cutler Braddock of the half-galley ship *Beaufort*), located at the southern end of the island. About seventeen years later, he began to build a house on the site, and by 1820 it was completed. Today most of the ruins of the Baynard Plantation are from that mansion.

The Stoney plantation passed by inheritance to a number of heirs until in 1840 "Saucy Jack" Stoney lost the property to William Eddings Baynard in an all-night poker game.

Baynard was already a successful planter on Edisto Island about thirty miles up the coast from Hilton Head, and he owned two other island plantations as well. He introduced Sea Island Cotton, which he brought from Barbados, onto his Braddock Point property. It soon flourished.

Baynard and his wife, Catherine, raised four children in the great house. In 1849, at the age of forty-nine, Baynard died of yellow fever. He was buried in an antebellum above-ground mausoleum in the cemetery of Zion Chapel of Ease, a tiny wooden Episcopal church that had been built for the plantation owners in 1788.

In December 1860 South Carolina was the first state to secede from the United States. By the time the war broke out, more than twenty working plantations were on Hilton Head Island, with the Baynard Plantation being one of the finest. Fortifications were built on the island in July 1861 to protect the area from Union forces, but that November, northern troops gained control over the region after winning the Battle of Port Royal.

More than ten thousand Yankee troops poured onto the island, but by then the Baynard family had fled. Union troops moved into their plantation house without a struggle, and they remained there, using the property as a headquarters through the end of the war.

Thinking that the Baynards might have hidden some of their treasure in the family mausoleum to recover later, looters broke into their tomb at Zion. No valuables were discovered—that is, unless you count the corpse of William Baynard. They emptied the sepulcher, including removing Baynard's body. His remains have never been recovered.

Sometime between August and December 1867 the manor went up in flames. Some think it was torched by a band of ex-Confederate raiders. Regardless, by the time Hilton Head Island was resettled after the Civil War, there was nothing left standing on the Baynard property, and there was no reason for the family to return. (They did go to court to regain legal title to the land about fifteen years later, but they never moved back onto the island.)

Today little more than a few foundations of the mansion remain. There are ruins of a few outbuildings, probably the quarters for the slaves who acted as servants in the main house, part of the chimney from the overseer's lodgings, and a small structure that most likely acted as reinforcement for Union tents. There's not much more to see. But that hasn't stopped the ghost of William Baynard from returning home.

In 1956 developer Charles Fraser opened Sea Pines Resort, a master-planned enclave designed as a family holiday destination. Hilton Head Island has grown in leaps and bounds ever since. It has become subdivided into private residential gated communities called "plantations" (not to be confused with the Civil War–era plantation estates), each offering its own blend of spas, golf facilities, beaches, and oceanfront views.

More than two million tourists now visit Hilton Head annually, and over the past half century, quite a few have been shocked to witness a most unusual sight: the ghostly funeral cortege of William Baynard.

According to the stories, on moonlit nights his ghost can be seen riding in a black-draped horse-dawn coach at the front of a funeral procession. His carriage is followed by the phantoms of his servants, dressed in plush red velvet, grieving for their master. The sad parade travels the old roads from the plantation ruins to Highway 278, heading toward the family mausoleum, which is near the intersection with Matthews Drive.

The Zion Chapel itself is gone, but the small cemetery remains. The Baynard mausoleum, built in 1846, is still there. In fact, it's the oldest intact building and the largest antebellum structure on Hilton Head Island.

The cortege stops at each plantation along the route. Baynard's ghost steps out of his coach, walks slowly to the gate, pauses briefly, and then returns to the carriage. It's said the spirit is searching for his body so he can return it to the family crypt.

If you see the ethereal parade go by, please give way. The restless spectre of William Baynard has been disturbed more than enough for one lifetime—and the next.

Chapter 9

John Brown's
Body

They say that if you really believe in a cause and your passion is strong enough, you'll never back down. You'll never let go. That certainly seems to be the case in Harpers Ferry, where its most famous visitor refuses to leave—even after death.

"Excuse me, sir, can you tell me where to find the entrance to the armory?"

"Wait, Brandon, let me get my picture with him. You don't mind, do you, sir?"

The man and his wife were taking the grand tour. Civil War buffs, they decided that during this summer vacation they would travel to as many important sites associated with the conflict as possible. Fort Sumter, Appomattox, Gettysburg, tons of other battlefields, and, of course, Harpers Ferry.

True, the failed 1859 raid by John Brown and nineteen followers on the arsenal at Harpers Ferry, West Virginia (at that time still Virginia), wasn't really part of the Civil War. The attack took place a full year before South Carolina seceded from the Union, but it nevertheless acted as a catalyst to the inevitable War Between the States.

So here were the two war buffs, more than a century later, taking in Harpers Ferry during the height of the summer tourist season. Years before they had visited colonial Williamsburg, Virginia, so they were thrilled to see the Harpers Ferry people also had actors in period costumes walking up and down the streets, posing for photos and acting out their roles as soldiers, shopkeepers, and housewives.

And that's why they thought the scruffy man in the tattered brown period vest with a small black dog by his side was also one of the artists. He certainly looked the part, but unlike the other street performers, this man seemed detached, disengaged, his eyes vacant. But, then, who knows? Maybe he was supposed to be playing the town drunk or the village idiot.

As Brandon positioned his wife for the photo, they didn't notice as the man slowly started to fade out of sight. By the time they looked back at him, the townsman had completely disappeared.

"Why, look, Brandon. He's gone. Well, that was rude."

If they hadn't been so busy convincing themselves they'd just been snubbed by some lowly street entertainer, Brandon and his wife might have realized that they'd just had an encounter with the man whose deeds 150 years earlier had brought them to that very hamlet—for they had just met the ghost of John Brown himself.

Also, if they'd been very lucky—depending upon your definition of "luck"—they might have run into another ghost from the Civil War days that haunts a particular walkway in Harpers Ferry. The corpse of one of Brown's cohorts who was killed in the assault on the armory was left in a narrow passageway between two buildings, to be picked apart by swine. Today that man's ghost frequents the shadowy lane known as Hog Alley.

The spirits of both Brown and his comrade have been seen time and again by both residents and visitors, during the day or at night all throughout the year, for more than a century. What could have happened there all those years ago that caused these two to have their souls indelibly printed on the ether at Harpers Ferry?

✛

John Brown's body lies a molderin' in the grave
John Brown's body lies a molderin' in the grave
John Brown's body lies a molderin' in the grave
And his truth goes marching on

Let's go back a few years.

Call him hero, call him traitor—the nineteenth-century abolitionist John Brown refuses to be forgotten. (He also apparently refuses to stay "a molderin' in his grave," despite what the popular Civil War–era song suggests.) Even in his own time Brown was on everyone's mind. Union soldiers marched to war singing "John Brown's Body" (whose tune, with new lyrics by abolitionist Julia Ward Howe, later became "Battle Hymn of the Republic") to remind them of their cause.

Many historians believe Brown's infamous raid on Harpers Ferry directly led to the outbreak of the war. No less than the great black leader Frederick Douglass said, "John Brown began the war that ended American slavery and made this a free Republic."

The story of Brown and his subsequent hauntings began long before Harpers Ferry. By the end of the 1850s, the issue of race and slavery had bitterly divided the country to its breaking point. Not only did much of the southern states' economy rely on the cheap labor that slaves provided, but plantation owners also considered them to be property.

Northern abolitionists, who felt that all men were born with the inalienable rights enumerated in the Declaration of Independence, sought the slaves' freedom. But realistically they knew that, short of war, little could be done to convince slave owners to release them from their servitude. The line was drawn as the western territories began to join the Union. As each new state was admitted, it had to declare itself as a free or slave-owning state.

Enter John Brown.

Brown was born in 1800 in Connecticut, the son of a tanner. All of the Brown family members were conservative Calvinists, and although he was not a churchgoer, John remained a strong Christian throughout his life. After his family moved to Ohio, Brown returned to the East at the age of sixteen to enter school, first in Massachusetts, then Connecticut. He wanted to become a Congregationalist pastor, but vision problems and lack of money forced him to abandon his studies.

He went back to Ohio to work in his father's tannery, then branched out on his own. After he married, he and his family moved to Pennsylvania, where Brown bought property and opened a successful tannery. On the side, he also raised cattle and was a surveyor. For a decade, Brown led a fairly conventional life for the times.

Contrary to later public perception, in the years before he became an abolitionist and fervent activist—some would say fanatic—Brown had a respectable, highly regarded career. He had become an expert sheep breeder, and in the mid-1840s he was widely recognized throughout the East as an authority on fine wool.

The seeds for the later course of Brown's life were sown in 1837, when Presbyterian minister, newspaperman, and noted abolitionist Elijah P. Lovejoy was murdered by a proslavery mob in Alton, Illinois. Brown was heard to proclaim, "Here, before God, in the presence of these witnesses, from this time, I consecrate my life to the destruction of slavery!"

Then two of Brown's children died, one of them a newborn, followed by his wife. Brown remarried and moved back to Ohio. Like many people, Brown's business was hit hard by the Panic of 1837, and in 1842 he was forced into bankruptcy.

In 1855 Brown heard from his sons living in the Kansas Territory that slavery advocates known as "Border Ruffians" were armed and starting to attack anyone harboring abolitionist sentiments. Families were being threatened or killed, and Brown decided his sons were in danger.

On the way to Kansas to help his sons, Brown, who by then was living in New York, stopped at an abolitionist convention in Albany. There he met several people who would provide financial support for his activities over the next several years, up to and including the attack on the federal armory in Harpers Ferry.

Not only was Brown repulsed by the violence of the proslavery advocates in Kansas, but he was also disgusted that abolitionist forces were doing nothing to fight them, other than offering lip service. On May 24, 1856, along with four of his sons, a son-in-law, and two other supporters, Brown killed five slavery-leaning homesteaders on Pottawatomie Creek, Kansas, chopping them to death with swords.

In retaliation, proslavery men from Missouri under Captain Henry Pate captured two of Brown's sons (ironically, two who had *not* taken part in the Pottawatomie killings) and burned down their farmhouses. In June, Brown and twenty-nine others successfully defended settlers in Palmyra, Kansas, against Pate. (Pate was captured in the fight, and a prisoner swap eventually resulted in the freedom of Brown's sons.)

In August another group of proslavery men from Missouri, three hundred strong, marched into Kansas, planning to destroy the abolitionist towns of Osawatomie, Topeka, and Lawrence. Brown's company, outnumbered seven-to-one, fought them guerrilla style from a forest along the road until Brown was forced to retreat. The skirmish brought Brown national attention.

A battle between the two sides was averted in September when the governor of Kansas intervened; Brown and three of his sons left Lawrence, heading back east. For the next two years, Brown made the rounds of abolitionists, raising money to allow him to make a major military stand against the slavers. Among his contributors were six wealthy individuals who collectively become known as the Secret Six (or the Committee of Six).

On October 16, 1859, Brown and nineteen others attacked the Harpers Ferry Armory. Their plan was to capture the ammunition stored there to use for future battles. They would arm slaves as they worked their way south and help them escape their masters. They vowed only to fight in self-defense. The goal was to cause financial ruin to the South, forcing the region to give up its hold on slavery.

At first there was no resistance at the armory because only one guard was posted. But once Brown and his men were inside, local merchants and militia blocked their escape. Shots were exchanged between the two groups, killing several on both sides. Brown's men retreated to the engine house inside the arsenal for protection.

A Baltimore & Ohio train that passed through town alerted Washington the next day, so by the morning of October 18, Brown was surrounded by ninety U.S. Marines under the command of General Robert E. Lee. He was given a chance to surrender, but when he refused, the marines broke down the door.

Ten of Brown's men were killed in the melee, five escaped, and seven (including Brown) were captured. In late October, Brown was put on trial for murder, conspiracy with slaves, and treason against Virginia. On November 2, he was convicted on all counts. For the next month Brown was allowed to send and receive mail from his prison cell, and his letters, many of which were widely reprinted in abolitionist-leaning newspapers throughout the North, made him a household name—and, to many, a martyr.

On December 2, 1859, Brown made his walk to the gallows. Among those in the crowd who came to see him die was John Wilkes Booth.

Brown's body may have been sent to his family farm in North Elba, New York, but his spirit stayed behind to walk the streets of the town where he gained his greatest notoriety.

Harpers Ferry remains a quiet, peaceful town, and it somehow manages to remain so even when it's overrun by summer sightseers. The storefronts down the main-street historical district have been carefully restored to their rustic 1859 appearance. But look beyond the fresh paint and the welcoming smiles and you might just catch a glimpse of the tortured ghosts of John Brown and one of his comrades-in-arms.

Chapter 10

The Nun's
Walk

For more than a century, the solitary ghost of a medieval nun walked one of the country trails in the tiny village of Borley in England. Care to take a stroll down the proverbial garden path? If so, you may not be doing it alone.

It was twilight, and Harry Price was stationed in the gazebo. It was now or never. It was May 18, 1938. After almost seven years of investigating the rectory, he'd be leaving the next morning.

Although he'd seen many interesting anomalies, he'd yet to witness any actual manifestations of ghosts. And the one he wanted to see most was the phantom nun.

Borley Rectory was constructed in 1863 by the Reverend Henry Bull while he was the parish priest in the small hamlet of Borley, in Essex County, about sixty miles northeast of London. It was a rather ordinary redbrick building, but almost from the time it was completed, the house—or at least its property—was haunted. The first to see the apparition were Bull's daughters, and they realized from the start that it was the ghost of a sorrowful nun.

The spectre sometimes floated over the wide expanse of the yard that lay behind the rectory, but most often she was seen drifting down a particular path on the far side of the garden at the edge of the Bull property. The girls nicknamed the trail the Nun's Walk.

The sightings happened often enough that, on at least one occasion, all four daughters saw the nun at the same time. The spirit usually appeared at dusk or at night, but from time to time, she would show up in broad daylight. It wasn't just the girls who witnessed the ghost. The Reverend Bull admitted he had seen the phantom, and the ghost also sometimes surprised guests by peeking in through the windows.

Villagers had been aware of the spectre long before the rectory was built. According to local legend, the land was on the site of a twelfth-century monastery. A nun from a nearby convent impetuously eloped with a monk from that monastery, and a fellow friar aided them in their escape. All three were caught. The brothers were hanged, and for breaking her vows, the nun was buried alive in the monastery wall. That's the story, and even though no records from the period show either a monastery or a cloister in that area, the centuries-old rumors persist up to this day.

After Henry Bull's death, his son Harry was appointed rector. During his tenancy at Borley and up until his death in 1927, the frequency of the hauntings increased considerably. In fact, while Harry Bull was pastor a new apparition appeared: a fully outfitted phantom coach, complete with a team of spirit horses. It would turn up the drive and come to a halt in front of the rectory before disappearing without a trace.

After Harry Bull's death, almost a dozen clergymen were offered the Borley position, but, perhaps because of the infamous ghost, none accepted until the Reverend G. E. Smith agreed to take the post in October 1928.

Reports of the hauntings appeared in London's *Daily Mail*, and they attracted the attention of a famous paranormal investigator of the time, Harry Price. He first visited the estate in June 1929 and, although the Reverend Smith and his wife didn't believe in ghosts, they told Price they had caught glimpses of dark, weird figures in the house. They also heard unexplained footsteps and whispers, and lights would sometimes go on in unoccupied rooms. They also thought they had seen the phantom nun out on the garden pathway—as had two of their maids.

The next month the Smiths left the rectory, claiming only that the old building was too uncomfortable. Three months later, the Reverend Lionel Algernon Foyster and his wife, Marianne, moved in. Before long, poltergeist-like activity began inside the rectory, including the appearance of messages scrawled on the walls in small, strange lettering.

Somehow, the Foysters were able to hang on for six years before leaving. Then Price made his big step: He decided that the chance to fully investigate Borley Rectory was too good to pass up, and he leased the house himself, starting in May 1937.

Now, standing in the garden and looking over the great lawn, Price was sad that his tenure was almost complete. He was pleased with what he had accomplished, but many of his goals were unfulfilled. Nevertheless, he had seen seemingly supernatural events himself. Bells left alone in empty rooms rang by themselves; he could swear that objects had moved on their own. But he had never personally seen the nun. It was all the more galling because just three months before, one of his fellow ghost hunters claimed to have seen her!

Originally, of course, his plan had been simply to explore every nook and cranny of the building. He had wanted to be able to set up controlled experiments, and that's exactly what he did. Along with a team of forty men, he kept a record of everything that happened, day and night, in the empty structure, anything that seemed out of the ordinary—even if he suspected, say, that the odd groan he heard was merely the normal settling of an old house or that the mournful moan coming from the fireplace was probably nothing more than wind blowing through an open flue.

Price had meticulously spoken to everyone he could find who had ever been connected with the rectory, and more than a hundred people told him they had witnessed hauntings firsthand: temperature swings, abnormal scents, unexplainable music, dogs barking at thin air, doors slamming on their own. Some claimed to have even heard the spectral horse and carriage pull up in front of the house.

Even though Price was intent on conducting a scientific study, he had also allowed three mediums, S. H. Glanville and Glanville's son Roger and daughter Helen to conduct séances in the rectory. He thought any messages that came through might lead to proof of an actual haunting.

In one of the first sittings, contact was made with Harry Bull. His spirit, which, of course, spoke through the medium, claimed a monk by the name of Father Enoch, or perhaps Fadenoch, was buried in the garden. Despite a subsequent search, no grave was ever found.

At another séance, a nun named Marie Lairre spoke through a ouija board, but it was not the spectral sister from the garden. This nun said she had been seduced by a man who promised to marry her, but instead, on May 17, 1667, he had murdered her and buried her in the basement of a building located there at the time. Lairre claimed she would haunt the property until her bones were found, given a consecrated burial, and a mass was given in her name.

Back in the gazebo, Price recalled that during a séance just two months earlier they had gotten one of the most disturbing messages of all. Helen Glanville was operating the planchette when a spirit named Sunex Amures broke through, declaring that later that night, at 9:00 p.m., he would start a fire in the hallway and burn down the rectory. The group seated around the table had reason to be worried: Spontaneous fires had inexplicably erupted in the past.

But that deadline had come and gone, and it was now time for the investigation to end. The next morning, with the last of his instruments packed away, Harry Price loaded the car, took one last look at the rectory, and made his way down the short drive to begin his trip back to London. He sighed. If only the nun had walked for him.

✠

Ironically, exactly eleven months to the day after the warning at the séance, the rectory *did* burn to the ground. But there was no supernatural cause. The new resident, Captain W. H. Gregson, had accidentally tipped over a paraffin lamp—coincidentally, in the hallway.

In 1940 Harry Price published a book on his experiences at the Borley Rectory, which he titled *The Most Haunted House in England*. In the report, he called his inquiry "the best authenticated case in the annals of psychical research" and concluded that lingering impressions ("spirits," if you will) of former occupants had caused all the paranormal phenomena.

Over the next few years Price would return to the site of his most publicized encounter with the Spirit World, hoping to see if there were any more clues to be found in the burnt-out ruins.

In August 1943 Price discovered a jaw and other skull bones in the cellar of the rectory. At first he was excited. Could they possibly be the remains of Sister Marie Lairre? Or had he found the skeleton of the phantom nun? But almost immediately he realized the answer was no. How could they be? The rectory wasn't built until hundreds of years after the nuns had died—if they had existed at all.

The remaining shell of the rectory was finally leveled the next year. Since Price's death in 1948, he has had many detractors, as have his methods and claims. But the fact remains that there are still a hundred years of sightings that have yet to be explained.

Rumors of ghosts at the rectory have refused to die. Even though the building is long gone, curious thrill seekers still visit the small town hoping to catch a glimpse of the phantom nun. But for now she seems to have vanished.

Chapter 11

Occurrence at the Creek Road Bridge

If you put five skeptics on a ghost hunt out in the middle of nowhere, you can be sure nothing supernatural is going to show up. Or will it? Imagine the shock when the men in our tale discover that someone may have been trying to deliver a message from the Beyond after all—just not in the way they expected it.

The other four guys in the van weren't really sure what they were doing there, but Shawn had talked them into it. And, well, whenever he cooked up some harebrained scheme it usually turned out to be worth doing—if only for laughs.

This time they weren't so sure. Standing on the Creek Road bridge at 11:00 p.m. in the crisp autumn air, with their teeth chattering and their toes going numb, they wondered whether this might have been an expedition better taken up in the middle of summer.

The whole area surrounding Camp Comfort County Park, just south of Ojai, California, has a reputation for being a hotbed of haunted activity. More than a dozen ghosts are said to appear on that stretch of Creek Road between Oak View and Ojai.

First of all, there are three ghost riders. One is a woman on horseback who appears each year on the anniversary of the day her horse got spooked by a snake on the trail and threw her to her death. The other phantom rider is a black-clothed headless horseman. The third is a headless motorcycle rider who chases unlucky motorists down the lonely highway.

The most famous Creek Road bogeyman, the Char Man, might not be a ghost at all. According to legend, a farmer and his son were trapped in their burning house in the hills just south of town during the massive brush fire that swept through Ojai Valley in 1948. The father was killed, but the boy, though horribly burned by flames, managed to survive. The pain of his injuries drove him out of his mind, however. For some reason—perhaps an insane attempt to try to save his father's life?—he literally peeled the skin off the old man's cadaver and hung him from a tree by the heels.

The boy, hideously charred, escaped into the forest. Before long he began to rush out of the woods and jump into the road scaring or even attacking motorists. And woe to anyone who is stupid enough to call out his name! Some believe the Char Man, deformed, repulsive, and deranged, is still alive. Others say, after so many years, that the young man has died and that it's his ghost that haunts passersby on Creek Road.

Then there are the spectres that haunt the concrete bridge spanning San Antonio Creek just about fifty yards north of the campground. One, the spirit of a murdered bride, still in her wedding dress, appears by the side of the road. The spectres of two young children dressed in 1800s clothing walk the bridge balancing on the rail, then fall to their deaths in the stream. There's a disembodied ghostly hand of a child that scampers along the same railing. And on rainy nights you can hear the screams from a school bus full of children that skidded off the bridge in the 1930s and plunged into the creek below.

But it wasn't one of these phantoms the young men sought that unnaturally chilly fall night. They were hoping to meet, or at least contact, the ghost of a woman who had become so despondent over her husband that, to escape her unhappiness, she tied one end of a rope around her neck, the other around the bridge railing, and then jumped off. Ever since, her melancholy ghost has been spotted walking the bridge or dangling by a rope over its side.

Shawn, a professional magician and author, had first heard the tragic story in a lecture by the well-known Ventura-based paranormal investigator Richard Senate. In fact, as part of the session the participants had visited the very bridge on which the five guys were now standing.

After that first ghost hunt, Shawn wanted to learn more. To help him on his nocturnal pursuit, he wanted people who had some knowledge, or at least an interest, in the supernat-ural, so he enlisted the help of some semireluctant friends who were fellow magicians. One of them, Scott—whom he had convinced to drive—was an innovative tinkerer and could find a novel way to solve just about any magical prob-lem posed to him. David was the intellectual, as well as the youngest of the bunch. Bill was generally acknowledged by his peers to have the best control of any of them over a deck of playing cards, and the last of the fearless foursome was Bill's friend, Richard. Out of the entire group, Richard was the only one who wasn't a magician. He was more of what you might call a "party dude" and was along primarily to have a good time: Hey, being out with buds beat sitting at home watching late-night TV any day of the week. And what if they actually found a ghost? Wouldn't that be cool?

So there they were, holding flashlights, a ouija board, and a tape recorder (well, actually it was a "boom box"—it was 1985, after all), standing on a haunted bridge. Get-ting there had been no easy task. The haunted six miles of

Creek Road run through one of the most out-of-the-way stretches of the Ojai Valley. The path's two lanes, often overhung with the low-hanging branches of ancient oaks, cut through a rural landscape of broad fields and pasture land that's crisscrossed by small streams that run down to gurgle their way along the sides of the road. A few solitary ranches and homes, built far back from the road, dot the low hills.

When it's dark, a drive along Creek Road can be especially unnerving. The lack of streetlights makes the environs jet-black, pierced only by the beams of car headlights, which cast deep, creepy shadows along both sides of the highway. Above your head, the stars and moon are so intense that they seem close enough to touch.

Scott had pulled his van to the side of the road, just a few feet from the bridge. The five men stepped out and were immediately immersed in inky darkness and a surreal stillness. Rather than provide comfort, the calm added a feeling of apprehension to the adventure. They turned on their flashlights, made a quick sweep of the surroundings, switched on the tape recorder, and stepped onto the bridge.

And . . . nothing. No sudden apparitions, no banshee wailing in the darkness. Nothing at all.

There was a collective sigh of relief. As much as the guys didn't want to admit it, they were just as happy *not* to run into some crazy entity. Ghost hunting is all well and good in theory, but who knows how you'll react if you're actually confronted by something from the Other Side?

Now confident they weren't going to be attacked without warning, they moved farther out onto the bridge. Nothing special about it. A typical back-road country bridge, just wide enough for traffic to safely pass.

Then Shawn felt it. Suddenly the temperature around him dropped by at least ten degrees. It was if he had stepped into a small, circular shaft of icy air. But there was no draft, no wind. It was just a column of cold air over a precise spot about halfway across the bridge. One by one, each member of his crew felt the ice-cold air for himself. It was there all right. Shawn hadn't imagined it. After a bit of investigation, they discovered that the cold spot didn't start on the pavement above the bridge. It was actually a vertical shaft of frigid air that extended all the way from the brook far below, up and through the bridge.

A common paranormal phenomenon, cold spots are thought to be either evidence of a ghostly presence itself or perhaps a portal through which spirits pass from one plane of existence to another. But if that's the case, thought Shawn, and this was where the suicidal wife had hanged herself, why was the cold spot located six to eight feet away from the railing?

Then it struck him: The bridge had been widened. The woman had lived in the area when the most common transportation was on horseback. To accommodate cars and the ever-increasing truck traffic that now serviced the valley, several feet had been added to each side of the onetime narrow bridge. The cold area near the middle of the road was where the side of the bridge and the railing would have been when the woman was alive; it still marked the precise location where she hanged herself.

It was time to go to work. They put down the heavy tape recorder and set up the ouija board on the pavement in the cold circle. Two of them rested their fingertips on the planchette, which had been carefully placed in the center of the board, and waited.

"Is there anyone here?"

No reply. Complete silence, and no movement on the board.

"If there is anyone here that can hear my voice, we would like to talk to you."

Slowly at first, then with increasing speed, the planchette began to move. As the pointer shifted from one letter to the next, the men jotted them down on a piece of paper.

The disappointment was obvious on the faces of the group, however, even dimly lit as they were beneath the overhead glow of the flashlights' beams. The letters the planchette were pointing to didn't spell out anything; even a true believer in the occult would have to admit that the sequence was pure gibberish.

Time and again they tried, with different questions and different people manning the planchette. But always the same result: a short, excited burst of incomprehensible nonsense, then nothing. For more than an hour and a half they tried. Then, frustrated, weary, and chilled to the bone, they reluctantly decided to call it a night.

Their mood was downcast as they walked back to the van. For all of the hope with which they had started the evening, their quest had been a failure. True, they *had* encountered a cold spot (which may or may not have had a natural explanation), but otherwise they had made no contact with the Spirit World. No voices, no messages, and certainly no ghosts. Scott started up the van, turned off Creek Road back onto the main highway out of Ojai, and before long the bridge was far behind them.

The next day Shawn started thinking about their nocturnal exploits. He had worked with ouija boards before, and this was the first time that virtually nothing had been spelled out as the planchette moved from letter to letter. True, in previous sessions the "answers" he received often had no correlation to the questions he had asked the spirits, but this time all they'd gotten was a jumbled mess. He checked and rechecked the letters they had marked down, but no matter how he split the letters into groups, he couldn't form a single recognizable word. There were no hidden messages.

Perhaps the problem was with the questions, he thought. Maybe if he checked the audiotape. He rewound the tape, donned a set of headphones, and hunkered down to listen to two hours of nothing.

As he expected, there were no surprises—at least at first. There was the small talk and the banter, their glee at finding the cold spot, the busy sounds of setting up the ouija board, the unanswered questions. But then Shawn realized that, for whatever reason, he hadn't turned off the tape recorder when they finished the session with the ouija board. He had kept it running the whole time they were packing up and setting off for the van. He could hear the gravel crunching under their feet as they left the bridge and headed down to the foot of the hill where Scott had parked. He heard them joking about why the spirits hadn't shown up.

"Maybe they were too busy tearing the van apart to talk to us."

"Yeah, maybe when we get there, the tires will be gone, and there'll be big red letters sprayed on the windshield, saying, 'You're not leaving.'"

"*What!*"

Stunned, Shawn stopped the tape. What was that? He quickly rewound the tape and listened again. A hoarse voice, definitely not one of the five men, whispered, "*What!*" Not a question, exactly; just a simple, strong declaration.

"What!"

Shawn's mind started to race. The voice on the tape was unquestionably female, but there had been no women with them the night before. In fact, they hadn't run into anyone the entire time they were at the bridge. The place was deserted. He replayed the tape. And again. The voice was definitely there!

Had there already been something on the tape the recorder failed to record over? Or had noise bled through from the other side of the tape? No, he distinctly remembered: Halfway through the night he had opened a brand-new tape on the bridge and put it into the recorder, and the boom box had never left his sight. Had he carried it in some way that he accidentally brushed the microphone and created what sounded like a person talking? Could someone have coughed or sneezed in such a way that it could be mistaken for a voice? Popping in a new tape, Shawn tried to re-create the sound, but to no avail.

He was startled by a hard, loud rap on the door and looked up. It was Scott.

"What's up, Shawn? You look like you've seen a ghost."

"Not funny, Scott. Listen to this."

Shawn told his friend about the unusual voice, placed the old tape back into the recorder, handed Scott the head-set, and hit Play. Though Scott was the hard-core cynic of the bunch, he dutifully put on the headphones. After just a few moments, a look of terror appeared on his face. Scott pulled off the earphones and threw them across the room.

"Man, what was that?! Don't ever play that tape for me again!"

"You mean you heard the voice?"

"Sure, I heard the voice. And the breathing too!"

What? Shawn realized he had never listened to the tape all the way through. He had always shut it off as soon as he had heard the voice. He plugged the headset back in, rewound the tape, and listened. Sure enough, there it was: *"What!"* followed a few moments later by the low but distinct sound of a person exhaling three times, once right after the other. And the most frightening part of all, the three breaths sounded much closer to the microphone than the voice had been. Whatever had made that sound had been standing in the middle of the five guys, right next to Shawn!

With an almost fanatic fervor, Shawn began to rethink the exact conditions of the night before. Richard had a slight cold. Could the breaths have been his? No. The boom box had two sensitive mikes that recorded in stereo. By listening carefully, Shawn could position each of the five men, identify their voices as well as their breathing, and tell how far they had been from the tape recorder. The exhaling that followed the mysterious *"What!"* on the tape had definitely not come from any of them.

Over the next few days, Shawn visited the other three men who had accompanied him that night to the haunted bridge. All of them heard the voice on the tape; all of them heard the deep breaths. All of them were dumbfounded. None of them had heard anything out of the ordinary that night, but they had to admit: It was there on tape.

Electronic voice phenomenon, or EVP, is defined as a form of paranormal activity in which the voice of a deceased person is picked up on electronic equipment, most often on magnetic audio tape. Almost without fail, no one hears the ghost voices when the recording is being made. They aren't noticed until the tape is played back. EVP is very,

very rare, so some say that is definitive proof of a world beyond our own.

Disbelievers say there is always some natural explanation for such sounds, some background noise that people just weren't aware of at the time of the recording and, therefore, couldn't recognize later. But for Shawn and the other four men who went on a ghost hunt that night more than twenty years ago, there wasn't any doubt. The occurrence was real. They were visited by one of the spirits of the Creek Road bridge.

Part Three

PHANTOM TRAVELERS

Spirits don't always stay close to home. They're often out and about, so it's little wonder they can pop up at any time and any place to surprise you.

Among our well-worn spirit travelers out on the highways every night are the Revolutionary War–era merchant Peter Rugg and General Anthony Wayne. There's the ghost driver who played host to Telly Savalas, Lincoln's funeral train, and the cursed car of actor James Dean. Then there's the story of a man who simply disappeared in the middle of his journey by coach across continental Europe. Was he captured by ghosts?

Chapter 12

The Long Ride Home of Peter Rugg

Getting home after a short trip shouldn't be a problem. But so far Peter Rugg has taken 275 years and still counting trying to do just that. Get out of the way if you see storm clouds forming in the middle of the road ahead of you: It just might be Peter Rugg coming through.

In 1820 it was no easy feat to make the long, difficult journey from New York City to Boston. Jonathan Dunwall, who was traveling on business, decided not to take the risky loop around Cape Cod at that time of year and instead settled on a quick packet ship transit to Providence. From there a two-day trip by stagecoach would set him safely in the Massachusetts capital.

Upon arriving in Providence, however, he discovered—much to his dismay—that every seat in the next carriage out was taken, so it was either wait until the following day for another conveyance or sit up front with the driver. Gratefully he accepted the proffered seat, and before long the group was on its way.

The ride and view were exhilarating, and within minutes Dunwall had fallen into animated conversation with the man holding the reins. The coach had carried on for several miles, bouncing down the well-traveled highway to the Cradle of Liberty, when suddenly the horses started to falter.

"What's the matter?" asked Dunwall. "Your horses haven't seemed skittish up to now. I don't see any trouble on the road."

"Ah, not yet, my friend. But just you wait. When the horses start to act up like that, there's a storm coming."

"And that's not all," he added. "In a few minutes' time, you'll be seeing something—or someone—that, well, that might not be of this world."

Dunwall scanned the skies. It wasn't yet dusk, although a few shadows from the trees lining the road were starting to stretch across the path in front of them. Still, it was bright enough for him to see that there wasn't a cloud overhead.

"I know what you're thinking," broke in the horseman. "But the man who's coming always brings a cloud of misfortune with him. He's what I call a storm breeder."

And with that, an extraordinary sight appeared on the horizon. A small, worn, open carriage pulled by a mammoth black bay horse came into view. Driving the chaise was a stout man, about thirty-five years old, dressed in the wardrobe of a colonial Dutchman of fifty years earlier—complete with breeches, several waistcoats, and a voluminous jacket with long cuffed sleeves. Sitting beside him was a young girl, about ten years of age, clutching her father's arm.

The mysterious driver was holding the reins tightly as his horse hurried forward at a steady pace. As the father and daughter passed the stagecoach, Dunwall noticed an anxious despair on the man's face. His eyes darted back and forth as if he were desperately trying to recognize his surroundings. Oddly, he and his daughter's clothing and hair were soaked, as if they had just emerged from a fierce rainstorm. The strange coach didn't pause, and its occupants barely looked in Dunwall's direction. Then, just as suddenly as the carriage had pulled up, it was gone, disappearing in the dust behind them.

"You've seen that man before?" asked Dunwall. "Under what circumstances?"

But before the coachman could answer, Dunwall felt something sprinkle on his brow. He looked up in astonishment. Despite the rest of the sky being absolutely clear, a black cloud was hovering above him, following quickly in the wake of the coach that had passed them. Lightning flashed all around, a peal of thunder boomed in their ears, and then all of a sudden, rain. A cloudburst. It only lasted a few seconds. Perhaps a minute. No more. The cloud then moved on, as if chasing the enigmatic wagon behind them.

"What did I tell you?" the driver murmured ominously. "A storm breeder."

Dunwall was astounded. In all of his travels, he'd never run into anything this fantastic. "If what you say is true, and you've seen this man and encountered such a bizarre storm before, you *must* tell me his story."

The driver confessed that he knew little about the peculiar man and the little girl. But he had seen them dozens of times while making his regular runs between Providence and Boston. Usually the coach simply rushed past. But the stranger *had* stopped to talk to him on a few occasions.

"He would always ask me the same thing. He needed directions to Boston. But he barely listened, usually grumbling in disbelief that he was so far from his destination. Then he'd take up his reins and rush off—more often than not in the wrong direction.

"I've asked about him all along the route. Others have seen him, too. Many others. And talked to him. He always asks the same thing, and no matter how much he's entreated to stop to eat, to take time to dry off, or to rest for the sake of his daughter, he always curtly replies that he must be on his way, that he has to reach Boston that very night."

It was getting quite dark. Making its break for the night about halfway to Boston, the stagecoach pulled up in front of Polly's Tavern. Soon the company had settled into the inn and found themselves seated at a long, narrow table, enjoying drinks, a fine repast, and a crackling fire to ward off the early autumn air. In short order, several pitchers of ale had been consumed, and talk among the travelers turned to the unusual man who had crossed their path earlier that day.

"Oh, yes, I've talked to him several times," offered one of the local residents who had insinuated himself into the conversation. "The Dutchman always asked me the quickest way to get back to Boston. As best as I can tell, he's never made it."

"In the course of a month, I ran into the man and his little girl in four different states," added a peddler.

"The poor lost souls," lamented a third. He didn't know how right he was.

More than three years passed before Jonathan Dunwall was to think about the "storm breeder" again. He was standing in front of Bennett's Hotel in Hartford, Connecticut, when he heard a man close to him call out in hushed tones, "There he goes again. It's Peter Rugg and little Jenny. He's nowhere closer to Boston. And he looks like he's seen a ghost."

"Perhaps," whispered a man next to him, "it's because he is one himself."

Dunwall looked out into the main street, disbelieving. The very same man and little girl he'd seen so long before, looking exactly the same, passed in front of his eyes. And over their heads floated a low, tight, dark thundercloud surrounded by streaks of lightning.

Dunwall could barely contain his excitement. "Forgive me for accidentally eavesdropping, my friends, but do you mean to say that you know who that man is?"

"Of course," they replied. "Everyone in these parts knows the sad story of Peter Rugg. But you won't believe it even if we tell you."

And if Dunwall hadn't seen the ghostly phenomenon for himself, he might not have.

One morning in the late autumn of 1769, just months before the massacre in Boston that presaged the first battles of the Revolutionary War, Peter Rugg, a wealthy cattle and horse trader, left his comfortable home on Middle Street in the North End of town for a short visit to nearby Concord. It promised to be a clear, sunlit day, so he asked his ten-year-old daughter, Jenny, to join him. Peter's wife, Catherine, waved good-bye to them as the light carriage pulled by Rugg's favorite horse, Lightfoot, made its way down the cobblestone road. That was the last time the unfortunate Mrs. Rugg would see her husband and child.

Rugg was respected, or at least tolerated, by his colleagues and neighbors. He was clearheaded, sober, and known for his good manners, decorum, and allegiance to the Crown. But he was also infamous for his short temper and obstinacy. When his mind was made up, he was intractable, and he was more than willing to share his opinions—quite vocally. In fact, once he got into a rage, he often blustered himself into a red-faced fury. And the language! But just as unpredictably as his anger would appear, so too it would instantly and inexplicably evaporate, leaving a composed, good-natured comrade and friend in its wake.

That day, with his business completed in Concord, Rugg started the seventeen miles back to Boston with his daughter. He was making good time when a late afternoon storm unexpectedly kicked up. Before he could find cover, the rain was upon them. Soaked to the skin, with the darkening sky slowing his passage, Rugg decided to stop briefly to rest at the home of a friend, a Mr. Cutter, in the village of Menotomy, just west of what is today Cambridge.

"Peter, you *must* stay the night!" Cutter implored. "It's now pitch black outside, and you'll hardly be able to see your way. The rain is even stronger than when you arrived, so it's no doubt making parts of the road impassable. If nothing else, think of the comfort and safety of your little girl."

But for whatever reason—pride? arrogance?—Rugg became stubborn and even more determined. The tempest cannot and will not stop me, he thought. No! And then, daring the fates, he swore the oath that would seal his doom forever: "Let the rains increase! I will see home tonight, despite this storm, or may I never see it again!" With that, he gathered up his cloak, and with his fearful, dumbstruck daughter at his side, he was out the door.

Back in the chaise, he whipped his horse with a hard flick. Startled, the bay jumped and began to force its way through the downpour. How terrible could the ride be? thought Rugg. It was only two more miles to the warmth and shelter of his manor on Middle Street.

But he never arrived.

Peter Rugg didn't make it home that night, or the next, or even the night after that. Although all of the likely routes were searched out of Menotomy, no trace of Peter Rugg, his daughter, Lightfoot, or the coach was ever found.

For many months after that, whenever the night turned stormy, Mrs. Rugg imagined that she could hear her husband's cracking whip, the hoofbeats of the horse, and the carriage wheels clattering down the cobbled street. Sometimes the neighbors, too, heard the commotion; it began to happen with such frequency that they began rushing to the windows whenever the distinctive noise was heard.

Then one night some of them saw it: Through the blanket of rain they could just make out the form of a large, black horse, then a carriage, and finally the outline of a man and a girl. It was Peter and Jenny Rugg! Valiantly they called to him and waved their lanterns, but the spectre didn't seem to hear or recognize them.

Instead his terrified eyes were glued to his own front door. His neighbors saw him pulling at the reins, so taut they looked like they would snap at any second. But the horse wasn't slowing its pace. If anything, Lightfoot was picking up speed. Then the apparition, seemingly unable to stop at the house, disappeared back into the blinding rain and out of sight.

The next day, with the skies cleared, friends of Mrs. Rugg began to make inquiries at all the public houses and stables in the area. Had anyone seen Rugg? Had he been able to bring his horse to rest at any of their establishments the night before? But, no. There was no sign of their missing neighbor.

Before long the familiar sounds stopped being heard, and residents of the district gave up any hope of seeing Peter Rugg again.

Some convinced themselves they had never seen his panicked face that wild and turbulent evening. Others decided the merchant had simply decided to desert his loving wife and home. Still others knew the truth: They had seen a ghost.

Soon rumors began to circulate that Peter Rugg's apparition had been seen in New Hampshire, Connecticut, Rhode Island, and even as far away as Delaware and Virginia. But never again in Boston.

Listening to the tale there at Bennett's Hotel, Jonathan Dunwall blinked. It couldn't be the same man in front of his eyes at that moment, could it? If the story was true, more than fifty years had passed since Peter Rugg lost his way along the road from Menotomy to Boston. Rugg would have to be more than eighty years old. And what about that little girl? It couldn't be his daughter. Why, she would be over sixty!

Dunwall could contain his curiosity no more. He had to know! He ran into the street and leapt in front of the carriage. The driver reined in the horse as Dunwall cried out, "Pardon me, kind sir. But are you the man they call Peter Rugg? Because I think I have seen you before on the road to Providence."

The man looked Dunwall over, considered for a moment, and then carefully spoke. "Yes, I am Rugg. And this is my daughter, Jenny. Indeed, you may have seen me near Providence. I seem to have become lost. We are headed to Boston. Can you please give me the most direct route?"

"Of course. But first, forgive me for being so forward, Mr. Rugg, but you seem quite weary from your travels. When did you leave home?"

"To be honest, I cannot say. It seems to have been a long time ago, but I've lost track of the days. But please detain me no further. I must be on my way. I will see my home tonight."

"Tonight?" exclaimed Dunwall in surprise. "But that's impossible. It's more than a hundred miles to Boston."

"Please don't try to deceive me, sir. Newburyport here is no more than forty miles from Boston."

There was a long pause. "I'm sorry, Mr. Rugg, but this isn't Newburyport. It's Hartford."

Peter Rugg was stunned, even though he had heard such news a hundred times before. How could it be? If this was Hartford, then that river he'd been following all day had been the Connecticut, not the Merrimack. How could cities, rivers, landmarks change their places overnight? Why could he never get back to his wife and home in Boston? Was he condemned to haunt these byways for all eternity? What demon had cursed him?

"Damn that oath!" And with that, Rugg shook the reins, and the phantom horse and carriage were off once more. The ghost of Peter Rugg turned the corner, back on his never-ending ride home.

Over the next century the legend of Peter Rugg was told in the pubs and hotels all along the main routes between New York and Boston. Occasionally there would be a burst of excitement when a toll collector on one of the local highways would burst into an inn, claiming the notorious spectre had just passed through his gate, or some traveler would profess to have given directions to a bewildered Knickerbocker desperately trying to get to Boston. But mostly, over time, as the number of sightings grew fewer and fewer, Peter Rugg was more or less forgotten.

But it's said that even today, if you're traveling on a back road in New England late at night, you might still cross paths with a weathered eighteenth-century wagon carrying a father and child. Pity them, tell them their journey is almost at an end, and give them directions to Boston.

Chapter 13

The Return of Mad Anthony Wayne

Some people just won't allow themselves to fade into the pages of history. They keep reliving their heroic deeds throughout eternity. Such is the case with that heroic Revolutionary rider in the storm, General Mad Anthony Wayne.

History? What could be more boring than that? Todd hated history class! Who cares about a bunch of old dead guys?

It was all just memorizing a bunch of names and dates long enough to pass the test, right? And this course, American history, had to be the worst. The country's only two hundred years old. How much history worth talking about could there be?

1492: Columbus rediscovers America after everyone forgets the Vikings got there first. Check. 1620: Pilgrims land on Plymouth Rock. Check. 1776: Duh. When it came to history, Todd really didn't care much about anything that had happened further back than his date on Saturday night. Now *that* made history!

"Class, open your books to page seventy-two," droned the teacher. "The Revolutionary War. Todd?"

Hearing his name, Todd stopped daydreaming and was back in the classroom. He squirmed nervously in his seat. Why did the teacher have to call on him?

"So, Todd, other than George Washington, who do you think was the most fascinating military figure in the war?"

Todd stared blankly. Was he supposed to have read something about the Revolutionary War? When was *that* homework given?

"Anyone?" asked the teacher without much hope.

A hand sprang up. Everyone groaned good-naturedly. Ashley. Of course, Ashley. *She* had an answer. She *always* had an answer. Her hand was the first to go up no matter what a teacher asked; she was always the first to want to offer an opinion, to discuss, to take a test, to write a term paper. What was wrong with that girl?

"Anyone *but* Ashley?" The teacher surveyed the room. She didn't know why she bothered. She knew that her prize pupil—even though she wasn't supposed to have favorites—was probably the only one who had done the assignment. With a well-worn sigh, the teacher gave in. "All right, Ashley."

What was she doing, wasting her life with eighth-graders? the teacher asked herself. She had been just like Ashley when she was in school: enthusiastic about learning, always eager to debate. She loved staying after class, talking to the teachers. After all, they were the only ones who seemed intelligent enough to carry on a conversation. Had she mistaken that passion for wanting to go into education herself?

But, then, there was Ashley and the one or two other students each year who seemed to make it all worthwhile. Whom would Ashley select? she wondered. Maybe Lafayette, the flamboyant Frenchman who decided to serve with the Americans. Maybe John Paul Jones, the dashing naval commander: "I have not yet begun to fight!" Or better yet, Benedict Arnold. Now there was a complicated man. Why had he turned traitor? She would love to hear what Ashley would say about that man.

Ashley beamed. She knew she would be called on, but somehow it still always seemed to surprise her when it actually happened. "I think I would have to pick General Wayne."

Silence. No one in the class seemed to have a clue whom she was talking about. "You know: General Anthony Wayne. *Mad* Anthony Wayne."

Suddenly Ashley had Todd's attention. We had a nutcase for a general in the Revolutionary War? he thought. This had to be good.

Almost as if she could read Todd's mind, Ashley quickly added, "Of course, he wasn't really crazy. He got the nickname because when he fought he used risky, unusual tactics that none of the other generals would have even considered. And, instead of staying safely in the back, Wayne always led the charge himself."

Todd had been had! So this Wayne character wasn't nuts after all. Pity. At least that would have made the class interesting.

"But that's not why I picked him," Ashley added. "It's because of his ghost."

You could almost hear the entire class take a giant, collective breath. A ghost? There was a Revolutionary War general who has a real, honest-to-goodness ghost running around? And people have seen it?

This was what the teacher prayed for more and more each day: some small, insignificant detail, some hook that would grab the students and hold their interest. And if it came from a student, all the better. Ashley started her tale.

Wayne was born in 1745 just outside of what is today Paoli, Pennsylvania. He was trained to be a surveyor, worked in his father's tannery, then later served in the Pennsylvania legislature.

Wayne signed on with the Revolutionary cause from the very beginning, raising a militia in 1775. Just a year later he was made the colonel of the Fourth Pennsylvania Regiment and fought with the Continental Army in its unsuccessful attempt to invade Canada. It was during this time that he commanded the troops at Fort Ticonderoga, service that resulted in his being promoted to brigadier general.

He would go on to fight throughout Pennsylvania, and he and his forces were holed up with George Washington's troops that bitter winter in Valley Forge. Afterward, Wayne was victorious in the Battle of Monmouth against the British, continuing to fight even though his army was far outnumbered.

Perhaps his most famous exploit during the war was his 1779 raid on the British fort at Stony Point, New York. The stronghold was built high on the side of a cliff overlooking the Hudson River in a seemingly impregnable position. Nevertheless, on the night of July 15, using only bayonets, Wayne and his men stormed the bastions and overtook the fortress. It was exactly the type of daring attack that earned Wayne his reputation for being "mad."

After the British surrender at Yorktown, Wayne moved south into Georgia to nullify the treaties between the British and the Native Americans and to convince the tribes to forge new alliances with the United States. Though promoted to major general, Wayne left the military in 1784 and served another a year in the Pennsylvania legislature before moving to Georgia, which had given him a sizeable plantation to thank him for his peace negotiations with the Creek and Cherokee.

The mad general returned to military life at the request of then President Washington to help fight the American Indians in the frontier territory of Ohio. To ready his troops, Wayne established the first regular training camp for American soldiers. He was returning from a command in Michigan in 1796 when he died from the gout. Wayne was buried in Erie, then later re-interred in the family plot at St. David's Episcopal Church in Radnor, Pennsylvania.

Nice, succinct biography, thought the teacher. Short, concise. All the major points. "Good work, Ashley. But what about the ghost?"

Ashley knew what everyone in the class was waiting for. She could see it in their eyes—especially Todd's. He was, she realized, kinda cute—that is, in a goofy, dumb-jock kind of way, if you liked that sort of thing.

Right: the ghost.

Mad Anthony Wayne may have died, she told them, but his spirit apparently won't stay in the ground. Take that burial in Pennsylvania, for example. Originally, Wayne was laid to rest at Fort Presque Isle, where the Wayne Blockhouse, named after the general, stands today. In 1809, Wayne's son Isaac asked to have his father's remains moved back to the family plot in Radnor. Wayne's corpse was dug up and, at a doctor's suggestion to prevent disease, was boiled to clear any lingering pieces of flesh off the bones. The soupy mix of tissue and fluid was then returned to Wayne's Erie grave, and just the bones were loaded onto a cart to make the 180-mile journey across the dusty, bumpy path over the Alleghenies to Philadelphia. Along the way, many of the bones fell off the carriage and were lost. Today much of that route forms U.S. Highway 322 in Pennsylvania, and according to legend, every January 1 (which happens to be Wayne's birthday), his spectre walks the roadway trying to find his missing bones.

Cool, thought Todd. He could almost picture the poor ghost, half human, half skeleton, trolling his way along the street looking for part of his skull or maybe his elbow.

But wait! That was it? He had to hear all that stuff about the Revolutionary War just to find out about one day a year that some guy supposedly shows up as a spook? Why, it was almost like he was tricked into learning!

Fortunately for Todd, Ashley wasn't through. "That's not all," she continued. "Since he was in the army, Wayne spent years of his life on the move. So it's not surprising that his ghost shows up all sorts of other places. Remember that time he spent at Fort Ticonderoga?"

It seemed the bachelor Wayne had quite an eye for the ladies, and they for him. As the commander of the fort, he naturally had a lot of young women competing for his attention and affection. He met such ladies at the same private dinner at the fort: Penelope Haynes, the daughter of a wealthy Vermont landowner, and Nancy Coates, a local girl.

Despite Penelope's higher status and her well-connected father, Nancy won out, and she and Wayne were soon a pair. Before long, it became apparent that Nancy wanted Wayne to marry her, but the matter didn't have time to come to a head because the British were closing in. Nearby colonists were asking for protection, so George Washington ordered Wayne to bring all the area women into the shelter of the fort.

Wayne set off to gather them, and rumor soon had it that the commander was in actuality going off to bring back Penelope Haynes so he could marry her. Indeed, Wayne soon returned with many women and young girls from the immediate surroundings, but the only one Nancy noticed was Penelope. Were the stories true? That night Nancy stole down to the shores of Ticonderoga. She tortured herself, crying, berating herself for not being pretty, or witty, or charming enough. Then, just before dawn, as the first rays of light were starting to gleam across the surface of the lake, Nancy strode out into the dark waters to her death.

Ever since, Nancy's ghost has walked the paths along the lake, reliving that horrible night. She's also been seen floating in the lake itself and inside the fort. For his part, Wayne's ghost has appeared in his old garrison quarters, either in the dining room or by the fire.

Although Wayne doesn't walk on the trails around Fort Ticonderoga, he does visit another lakeside. During the Canadian campaign in 1776, Wayne captured two baby eaglets along the banks of Lake Memphremagog, which is located near Newport, Vermont, on the border with Quebec. His hope was to train them for hunting, and, indeed, from then on he traveled with the birds almost everywhere he went. He was so devoted to them that his ghost has now returned to the shores of Memphremagog. He's seen strolling along the path at the water's edge, dressed as a frontier scout and holding the eagles, falconer-like, one on each wrist.

But perhaps the most terrifying manifestation of Mad Anthony takes place on the mountain road through Storm King Pass outside Cornwall, New York. He appears as a phantom horseman, re-creating one of the most courageous and audacious rides of his career.

In 1779 George Washington ordered Wayne to issue warnings to the American soldiers located along the Hudson River about British forces in the area. Wayne, who was familiar with the trails, set out on his favorite horse, Nab, under cover of night in a turbulent rainstorm, passing through Storm King Pass to alert the troops. He returned safely, only to immediately turn around and lead his men against the barricades at Stony Point.

"And to this day," Ashley said, finishing her tale, "just before a big rain hits, the ghost of Mad Anthony Wayne appears on the windswept mountain roads of Storm King State Park. The spectre, wearing a full cape that whips behind him, is on horseback. He's riding Nab, and the hooves of his spirit steed shoot sparks as they pound against the highway. The pair rushes down the road, dashing through the tunnels that now pass through the hills. If you see them coming, move aside, because the general is on a secret mission—a mission that he now carries out, over and over for all time."

Wow, thought Todd. Secret missions. Ghost stories. Girls killing themselves over you. Maybe history isn't so bad after all. Lost in his thoughts, he let a small grin cross his lips. The teacher saw it and smiled.

Chapter 14
The Man Who Disappeared

Can a person simply vanish right before your eyes? One second he's there; the next instant he's gone. That's what happened to highway traveler Benjamin Bathurst back in 1809, and they've been looking for him ever since!

People go missing all the time. Sometimes they simply get tired of their lives and strike out to reinvent themselves. Some go off on reckless adventures without telling anyone and never make it home. Still others are victims of foul play. But then there are those who just disappear, without a trace, with no possible explanation. To paranormals, this last group is the most fascinating, of course, because it suggests that the person might have somehow been able to instantly travel into another dimension or plane of existence—or that he or she has been snatched by someone in the Unknown.

Here are the basic facts of just such a story: Benjamin Bathurst was a young British diplomat at the beginning of the nineteenth century. He was envoy to the Imperial Court in Vienna, Austria, where he met with Emperor Francis. On November 25, 1809, he was returning to England by coach and had stopped to eat at a tavern in Perleberg, Prussia. After dinner he went out to inspect his horses in the company of his valet and a personal secretary. Then, according to their testimony, Bathurst "walked around the horses" and was never seen again.

When Bathurst didn't complete the circle around the stagecoach or come back around to join them, his puzzled companions went to check on him. But Bathurst was gone. There was no sign of a struggle or violence. There had been no screams, shouts, or cries for help. No sound of a gun fired or a saber drawn. Not even hasty footsteps of an assailant or kidnapper rushing down the cobblestone street. Bathurst had somehow instantaneously vanished from the face of the earth.

People don't just disappear. Or do they?

Bathurst was born in September 1784 as the third son of the bishop of Norwich in England. He married Phillida Call, the daughter of a titled Cornish property owner, Sir John Call. Bathurst entered the diplomatic corps at a delicate time in Europe. The Napoleonic wars had begun, and England was eager to gain Austria as an ally and, if possible, convince the country to declare war on France. In 1809 Earl Bathurst, the secretary of state for the Foreign Department and a distant relative of Benjamin's, sent the young envoy to the court of Emperor Francis to press England's concerns. At first, the mission seemed to have been a success. In April of that year, the emperor moved soldiers into Italy to counter Napoleon's forces.

But Bonaparte was a superior strategist. Napoleon attacked Austria itself and, after a stunning defeat at the Battle of Wagram in July, the French captured Vienna. As Austria sought to make peace with France, Bathurst was called back to London.

Although his country was supposedly neutral at that point, Bathurst knew his situation was perilous. Napoleon's forces would no doubt consider him at best an intruder into their affairs and at worst a spy. He was, at the very least, the agent of a foreign government. Even with diplomatic immunity, he was far from safe as long as he remained on the continent.

The quickest route back to England would have been south to the Adriatic. Once at sea he probably would have encountered little opposition crossing the Mediterranean, but getting to the ship would have been extremely dangerous. So after careful consideration Bathurst decided his best bet to get home safely would be to travel north, through the German Confederation to Hamburg on the Baltic.

Disguising himself Bathurst traveled as a German merchant named Koch, and his secretary pretended to be his courier. Soon he was in Prussia, which was also still neutral in the Napoleonic conflicts. Bathurst stopped briefly in Berlin, then continued on to Perleberg, where he arrived about noon.

At that time, Perleberg on the Stepnitz River was little more than a military outpost on the border with France. Prussian solders were stationed there, and French militiamen were just to the south in Magdeburg. The rough-and-tumble town was filled with the sort one would expect in such a frontier settlement—army officials, camp followers, ladies of negotiable affection, traders, peddlers, and a cast of shady characters that included turncoats, secret agents, and thieves.

Bathurst stopped his carriage at the post house, ordered new horses for his onward journey, and then went to dine at the White Swan, a tavern just a short distance away. He took a room at the inn, where he composed some letters, destroyed other documents, then lay down for a few hours of sleep. After dinner, he decided that, rather than stay a full evening at the hostel, it was best that he and his traveling companions get under way. Strangers attract too much attention if they stay very long in one place, and the dark would help cover their departure.

At about 9:00 p.m., Bathurst, followed closely by the other men, went out front of the inn to overlook as his trunks were being loaded onto the coach.

Then it happened.

As recounted in an article by Sabine Baring-Gould, a nineteenth-century English essayist and clergyman, Bathurst "stood outside the inn watching his portmanteau, which had been taken within, being replaced on the carriage, stepped around to the heads of the horses—and was never seen again."

Bathurst's secretary, who had been paying the landlord, looked back to the carriage. Where was his master?

"Herr Koch? Are you there?"

When there was no response, the courier circled the coach. His master was gone. He waited a few minutes, bewildered. It was not like Bathurst to venture out on his own, especially when they were in such dodgy circumstances. And the horses seemed to be nervous and unsettled—what had spooked them?—so the secretary shouted out again, this time more forcefully.

"Herr Koch. Please, where are you?"

It was a call that would never be answered.

The valet and secretary waited nearly an hour for Bathurst's return. At first they were puzzled but not terribly concerned. Well aware of Bathurst's mission, they assumed he had surreptitiously slipped away to make some last-minute covert preparations. But eventually, when Bathurst never showed and with no instructions or other alternative, the servants were forced to go to the mayor and reveal their situation.

There was an official inquiry as to Bathurst's disappearance, of course. No one else had been seen near the carriage, but it was very dark in the courtyard, the sun having set a full four hours earlier. If someone had been lying in wait and was skilled enough to immediately silence his victim, Bathurst might have been surprised by assailants, overtaken, and then quietly dragged away. But that's a lot of ifs.

And who would have done such a thing, and why? Well, there was no disagreement on that point. There were dozens of people in the town who might have wanted to do in a well-dressed traveler. And as Kraus, the valet, pointed out during the investigation, after supper Bathurst had been "standing before the kitchen fire, in the midst of the postillions and ostlers . . . carelessly pulling out his watch, and likewise his purse, containing a considerable sum of money." He added that he thought it was very likely that one or two of them could have "taken an opportunity of hustling him away, and afterwards robbing and destroying him."

Then, too, Bathurst's clandestine travel plans might have been compromised by undercover spies anywhere on the road from Vienna. In fact, his true identity had apparently been an open secret in Berlin. Could he have been abducted by agents of the French government? For years rumors persisted that soldiers had captured Bathurst and jailed him in the fort at Magdeburg, but any such accusations were always denied.

Prior to his departure, Bathurst had considered the possibility that there might be an attempt on his life. Before working on his papers, he had visited the military commander in Perleberg, Captain Klitzing, and asked for protection. He was assigned two guards but, apparently to avoid suspicion as he boarded his coach, Bathurst released the guards around 7 p.m. This led Klitzing to later suggest that Bathurst must have wanted to flee, undetected, on his own.

Nevertheless, the captain dragged the river, looking for a body. At the same time he launched a house-to-house search. Just a few days later, Bathurst's fur coat was discovered hidden in an outhouse owned by Auguste Schmidt, one of the staff at the White Swan. He claimed, however, that his mother had simply kept the coat after Bathurst left it behind. Then, about a month later, the diplomat's pants—just his pants—turned up in a forest about three miles outside of town. But still no trace of Bathurst himself was ever found.

Despite Klitzing's investigation, a prolonged personal search by Mrs. Bathurst (which included an audience with Napoleon), and inquiries made by three private detectives, no real evidence of foul play was ever discovered. At least three skeletons of murder victims were uncovered in Perleberg in the next few decades, but none of them was ever definitively identified as Bathurst.

So the story remains a mystery. But why has it obtained such fame in the annals of the supernatural?

In the early twentieth century, noted investigator of anomalous (or unusual) phenomenon Charles Fort ran across the story, and he promoted the case as a perfect example of an unexplained disappearance. The vanish was sudden, direct, and almost elegant in its simplicity. The tale is classic Fortean because one of the possible solutions for Bathurst's disappearance, and indeed the most tantalizing to consider—that he was abducted by spectral beings or somehow spontaneously passed into another dimension—falls outside of accepted scientific principles. As a result the story has been revisited time and again by occultists, skeptics, and paranormal researchers.

Had Bathurst been captured by secret agents or held up by a simple robber? Had he decided, for reasons of his own, to simply become a "missing person"? Or had something more miraculous taken place? Did he somehow leap—body and soul— into the Next World? The debate continues.

Chapter 15
The Ghost Train

It's not just the souls of the dearly departed that haunt our nation's highways. Drive along any of the roads next to the deserted tracks of the old New York Central Railroad on April 27 and you may catch a glimpse of a ghost train—the funeral train that bore the casket of Abraham Lincoln from Washington, D.C., back to Springfield, Illinois, for burial.

"The president is dead."

The words reverberated in Jim's head as he drove westward along the lonely stretch of old State Highway 5 in central New York. What must it have been like in 1865 to hear such startling news: that our nation's president, the man who had fought so hard to keep our country united, had been struck by an assassin's bullet? Such a thing had never happened in our young nation's history. The shock must have shaken our war-weary country to its core.

Today many Americans believe Abraham Lincoln was the greatest president the United States has ever produced. But on the evening of Good Friday, April 14, 1865, when Lincoln was shot at Ford's Theatre, that wasn't necessarily the case. Like our nation at the time, our citizens' sentiments were deeply divided, with many admiring our sixteenth president's vision, courage, and strength, but with just as many reviling him.

After all, Lincoln had just led the country through the most troubled part of its history. Torn apart over the issue of slavery, the North and the South had just completed a bloody war that, in some cases, had pitted father against son, and brother against brother. In the aftermath of the conflict, many people believed it was Lincoln who had saved the country during its bitter struggle. But others, like his assassin, John Wilkes Booth, blamed Lincoln for destroying their very way of life.

Jim was keenly aware of all this as he drove that night outside of Schenectady. In fact, he knew he was following almost the identical path that had taken the president to his final resting place in Springfield.

After his tragic murder Lincoln became the first president to lie in state in the White House. His body was then carried by a train dubbed the Lincoln Special in a 1,700-mile grand funeral procession from the nation's capital to Illinois for burial. A cadre of soldiers escorted the president's body, and three hundred mourners accompanied his coffin. Also on the train was the casket of Lincoln's son Willie, who had died in Washington in 1862 at the age of eleven and was disinterred for reburial with his father.

Although not widely publicized, an undertaker and an embalmer were on board, and their only job was to keep the president's remains looking presentable during the journey. In addition, the casket was surrounded by flowers, with an increasing number of floral bouquets as the trip wore on, in large (though unspoken) part to cover the smell of decomposition.

The entire train was draped in black. The coffin, carried in a specially designed hearse railroad car, rested on a dais draped in black and covered overhead by a canopy held up by four columns decorated in black feathers, flags, and crepe. The mahogany coffin was lined in satin and silk and trimmed with black-and-white braid.

The upper third of the coffin's lid could be thrown back to reveal the president in his final repose. In death his ashen face was not diminished. His unmistakable features—the deep wrinkles carved into his countenance, the heavy, furled eyebrows—were merely frozen into immortality.

During its trip, the Lincoln Special took an unusually long route, with several out-of-the-way stops so the maximum number of Americans could pay their respects as the cortege rolled by, paused in a train station or stopped for a few hours in one of the larger cities to allow the casket to be removed and lie in state. The train passed through 445 communities along the way, and residents turned out by the tens of thousands—all total, about a third of the people living along the track's route viewed the funeral train.

From the beginning there were supernatural manifestations surrounding the funeral cortege. Many people claimed that as the train traveled through a town all the clocks in the station came to a standstill, and several individuals said their own pocket watches stopped as well.

Jim had heard the more recent stories, that in the years since the train made its fateful journey in 1865, people driving along the roads that parallel the rails on which the procession traveled had claimed to see a ghost train on the tracks every year on April 27. And if they listened closely, they could hear the faraway whistle of the train or the sad strains of the military band that was on board drifting through the night air.

The ghost train had been seen at various spots along the original route, all the way from Washington across New York, Pennsylvania, Ohio (especially between Urbana and Piqua, where the train passed on April 29 and 30), Indiana, and into Illinois. This April 27, however, Jim was driving along the most actively haunted stretch of the route, the section between Albany and Schenectady, New York. He wondered, would he see the train tonight?

Back in 1865 the funeral train had departed the District of Columbia on April 21 and made stops in such major cities as Baltimore, Philadelphia, and New York City before moving on to Albany. It arrived in the state capital sometime after midnight on April 25, and it remained there until the next afternoon. For the next two days, the train slowly made its way across New York, passing through Syracuse, Palmyra, and Rochester before arriving in Buffalo in the early morning of April 27.

So here was Jim, tracing the path of the funeral train on the anniversary of its passage. If he was going to see its ghost, tonight had to be the night. Consulting the road map he had lying open on the passenger seat beside him, he wondered where the best place would be to stake out the tracks.

Today the entire route can more or less be driven on the modern I-90 from Albany to Buffalo. But it's possible to get even closer to the old tracks, because before the Interstate Highway System was established, the rails were paralleled by a series of smaller highways and roads, including State Routes 5, 5S, 69, 365, 31, 33, 63, and 20.

The details of all these highways were important to Jim, because he knew most of the sightings had occurred on these smaller roads. He decided to try somewhere along the fifty miles of Route 5 between Schenectady and Utica, where the rails ran along the banks of the Mohawk River.

Jim had been attempting to catch a glimpse of the ghost train for years, ever since he first ran across a description of the haunting in the archives of the *Albany Times:*

It passes noiselessly. If it is moonlight, clouds cover over the moon as the phantom train goes by. After the pilot engine passes, the funeral train itself with flags and streamers rushes past. The track seems covered with black carpet and the coffin is seen in the center of the car, while all about it in the air and on the train behind are vast numbers of blue coated men, some with coffins on their backs, others leaning onto them.

At exactly midnight, Jim pulled his car into a turnoff by the side of the road. Here on Route 5, far from the city lights of Schenectady, he could just make out a piece of the old tracks that lay between the road and the nearby Mohawk River. He rolled down his car windows, tilted the seat back just a bit, and waited. The night's vigil had begun.

It was already spring, but the April night air was still crisp. There was a moon, but lazy clouds kept drifting across its face so the night scene was bathed alternatively in light and shadows. All seemed to be at peace.

Perhaps too much peace, thought Jim. Odd. He noticed that all of the insects had suddenly become quiet. He got out of the car, leaned against the door, and immediately felt overwhelmed by an eerie stillness.

And then he saw it: At first a hazy mist seemed to hover above the train tracks far off to his right, just where the rails met the horizon. Then the fog seemed to take shape. Was it possible? Incredibly, he could make out a large nineteenth-century-style locomotive steam engine emerging from the haze, billowing out puffs of smoke from its stack. But there was no sound of wheels rattling against the iron rails. It was the ghost train!

Softly, the sorrowful sound from the train's whistle cut through the air. Then the engine passed directly in front of him. Jim could clearly make out the crew in the open compartment: The train was being manned by skeletons.

Before he could react, the strains of a somber dirge floated to Jim's ears. It was the saddest, most melancholy melody he had ever heard. Where was it coming from? There: Just a few cars behind the engine was a compartment in which sat a spectral uniformed concert band, all skeleton musicians, playing the solemn requiem on phantom instruments. As he watched, transfixed, mesmerized, the other cars passed by, filled with the spectres of hundreds of Union soldiers.

On one of the last cars of the funeral train, Lincoln's casket was clearly visible through the black-curtained windows. An honor guard of skeletons, wearing their Union dress blues, surrounded the coffin. The only thing missing was Lincoln's ghost. Then one of the most interesting parts of the legend was true, thought Jim: Despite the countless times over the past century the funeral train has been spotted, no apparition of the president himself has ever been seen on any of the coaches.

With one last cry of its whistle, the train hurtled on, disappearing into a vapor that hung over the tracks. It was gone.

Jim remained speechless, spellbound and unmoving as he reflected on the miracle that had just occurred. He glanced down at his watch. It was still midnight. How could that be? Had time simply stopped to allow the ghostly train to pass through the world of the living? Although he knew he could never fully understand the phenomenon he had witnessed, Jim felt satisfied. He stepped back into his car, fastened the seat belt, and pointed his car west. He still had a long drive to Buffalo.

✥

Well, you know what they say: You can't keep a good ghost down. Although Lincoln's ghost doesn't appear on his phantom funeral train, his apparition *has* appeared in a number of other spots associated with both his life and death.

The next time you're in Washington, D.C., you might bump into Lincoln yourself if you take a tour of the White House, because he has most often been seen and sensed still "living" at his most famous address, 1600 Pennsylvania Avenue. The first person to report seeing Lincoln's ghost there was Grace Coolidge, the wife of President Calvin Coolidge, and it happened during their time in the White House, from 1923 to 1929. She abruptly entered what she thought was an empty Oval Office to confront the shadowy silhouette of the former president standing at one of the tall windows in deep sorrow, looking out toward the Potomac.

Lincoln's spectre most often haunts the bedroom now known as the Lincoln Room. Many people who have stayed there overnight have heard spectral footsteps walking up and down the hallway outside the room, and at least one guest was startled upon entering the room to see the ghost of Lincoln sitting at the foot of the bed, pulling on his boots. During Ronald Reagan's years at the Executive Mansion, his daughter, Maureen, also saw Lincoln's apparition there.

During the administration of Franklin Delano Roosevelt, Queen Wilhelmina of the Netherlands paid a state visit to the White House, and she stayed in the Lincoln Room. In the middle of the night, she heard footsteps in the hall, followed by a knock at the door. She opened it and was startled to see the full-form ghost of Lincoln, standing in top hat and frock coat. Needless to say, she immediately fainted; when she awoke, the spirit was gone.

Other residents, including Eleanor Roosevelt, Teddy Roosevelt, and Jacqueline Kennedy, have felt a presence in the White House that they were certain was Lincoln, although they never saw an actual apparition. Eleanor's dog, Fala, often looked out into a seemingly empty hallway and barked, as if trying to scare off an invisible intruder that many thought to be Honest Abe. After a visit to the Oval Office, poet Carl Sandburg said he had sensed Lincoln's spirit lingering near the windows. And disembodied footsteps heard on the second floor have long been attributed to Lincoln. Among those who admitted hearing the ethereal sounds was Harry Truman (who also confessed that some of his White House staff actually saw the ghost).

Before we leave Pennsylvania Avenue completely, you might be interested to know that Lincoln's ghost isn't the only presidential spectre that haunts the White House. The apparitions of at least three other presidents have been seen or experienced there. The melodic strains of an invisible violin wafting from the Yellow Room have been attributed to Thomas Jefferson, who played the instrument and was the first president to reside in the White House. Andrew Jackson appears in his old bedroom, now known as the Queen's Bedroom (also known as the Rose Bedroom), and the throaty, rough spectral laughter sometimes heard in the room is thought to be his. Some say banging sounds in the attic come from the ghost of William Henry Harrison.

Not all the late presidents haunt the White House, however: If you want to run into the ghosts of Presidents John

Quincy Adams and James Garfield, you'll have to walk down the street to the Capitol building, where they've taken up residence.

And if you happen to walk down First Street while you're making your way to Capitol Hill, you might also bump into the troubled ghost of Judge Advocate General Joseph Holt, who's seen wearing a blue suit and a cape. Holt presided over the Military Commission's trial of Mary Surratt and three others who were found guilty of conspiring to assassinate Lincoln. He's thought to be walking in the night air contemplating whether his verdict was correct.

But back to Lincoln's ghost. After he was mortally wounded, Lincoln was carried to Petersen House, a boarding house across the street, where he suffered for nine hours before dying. Lincoln's ghost has subsequently appeared there from time to time.

A young couple had shared the State Box in Ford's Theatre that tragic evening, Major Henry R. Rathbone and his fiancée Clara Harris. John Wilkes Booth stabbed Rathbone in the arm several times and severely injured him as the killer fought to escape. Rathbone was rushed off to a hospital, but Harris stayed with Mrs. Lincoln and sat vigil with her in Petersen House.

After the president's funeral, Harris soon returned to her family's summer cottage in Loudonville, New York, located about two miles north of Albany. (Clara's father, Senator Ira Harris, was a former jurist and a good friend of Lincoln. He was also Rathbone's stepfather, having married the soldier's mother after the death of her husband.)

Clara kept the white satin dress she had worn to the theater, still stained with the president's blood, and carefully hung it a closet at the house in Loudonville. Exactly one year later, she was awakened in the middle of night by Lincoln's ghost, laughing as he had been moments before the fatal shot was fired. The incident was dismissed as a dream until, years later, the governor of Massachusetts also saw the phantom during an overnight visit.

Rathbone walled up the closet, and the dress remained there undisturbed for more than a decade. The events in Washington had shaken Rathbone so much that, over the years, haunted by memories and regret, he sank into deep melancholia and suffered anxiety and delusions. On Christmas morning 1883 while in Hanover, Germany for medical treatment, he shot his wife Clara, killing her, and then slashed his left arm five times, perhaps in a bizarre recreation of that dreaded night at Ford's Theatre. In 1910, one of their sons, believing that the stained dress had somehow cursed his family, tore open the cottage wall, removed the gown, and burned it.

Lincoln's ghost has also been spotted at Fort Monroe, located in Hampton, Virginia. Way back in 1609, Captain John Smith (of Pocahontas fame) constructed a fort on the same site, and a series of fortresses were built there over the succeeding years until the present Fort Monroe was completed in 1834. The fortress played a key role in the defense of the Union during the Civil War, and Lincoln moved quickly after the South's secession to reinforce the fortifications. It was from Fort Monroe that Major General Benjamin Butler pronounced that the North would not return escaped runaway slaves to their former masters in the South. And it was there that Jefferson Davis, president of the Confederacy, was confined for two years after his capture in 1865. Perhaps it was Lincoln's deep commitment to preserving the Union that draws his ghost back to this important, historic fortress.

Finally, Lincoln's tomb itself is haunted. Located in Oak Ridge Cemetery in Springfield, Illinois, the elaborate mausoleum is 177 feet tall and is topped with several statues of the Great Emancipator. Almost immediately after Lincoln's burial, his enemies attempted to steal his body, either for ransom or for desecration. In 1901 Robert Todd Lincoln, the first son of Abraham and Mary Todd Lincoln, had his father's coffin exhumed and then re-interred under several feet of concrete to protect it. Rumors persist to this day, however, that the casket wasn't really returned to the tomb but was secretly buried elsewhere to guard against its theft. (Interestingly, the phantom funeral train has never been seen arriving at Springfield. Is this because Lincoln's body is no longer in the tomb there?) Whether Lincoln's body actually resides in the mausoleum remains a mystery. But footsteps attributed to the Illinois Rail-Splitter have been heard at his gravesite, and Lincoln's ghost has been seen hovering over the crypt (although with much less frequency).

As for the phantom funeral train: Does it still materialize today? According to legend, as long as there is anyone alive who grieves for the fallen president, the ghost train will continue to appear. If you're driving along I-90 or New York State Highway 5 on a late April's eve and look to the old railway tracks, you, too, may experience the ghost of Lincoln's funeral train for yourself.

Chapter 16
Telly's Phantom

The most famous highway ghost story of all is that of the phantom hitchhiker. But what would you say if you found that the person who gave you a lift when you needed one turned out to be a ghost? Maybe in the Spirit World, turnabout is fair play.

"Who loves ya, baby?"

That phrase, heard everywhere in the 1970s, was the trademark of Kojak, TV's bald, lollypop-licking New York City police detective, portrayed by charismatic actor Telly Savalas.

Born Aristotelis Savalas on January 22, 1922, in Garden City on Long Island, New York, the popular TV and film actor was the son of Greek Americans. His father owned a restaurant, and his mother was an artist. Young Telly served as a soldier in World War II, then worked in a variety of jobs—as a lifeguard, a newspaper vendor, and, for a time, a journalist for ABC News. All down-to-earth, real-world jobs. It was this background that Savalas was able to bring so effectively to his signature role as Lieutenant Theo Kojak.

Telly's first acting experience was in episodic television, but by 1962 he had also begun to branch out into movies, appearing in such films as *Cape Fear* and giving an Oscar-nominated supporting performance in *Birdman of Alcatraz*. He shaved his head for his standout role as Pontius Pilate in 1965's *The Greatest Story Ever Told,* and it was such a strong, distinctive look that he kept it throughout his long career. He became known for playing tough guys with a soft streak or an edgy sense of humor, so the role of Kojak was an easy fit. Little wonder he was identified with it for the remainder of his life.

Even for actors, there's always a definite line between reality and the world of make-believe. But all that changed for Savalas when he had a life-altering brush with the Unknown. The encounter haunted the actor until he died in 1994, one day after his seventy-second birthday. His experience was one of the rarest of ghost phenomena: He was actually a passenger in a phantom car!

When you think of Long Island, the first thing that comes to mind usually isn't a dark, deserted highway. After all, the island's western boundary is just across the narrow band of the East River from downtown Manhattan, home to more than 1.5 million souls. On Long Island itself, you'll find another 4 million people living in just the Bronx and Brooklyn. But as you move farther out on the island, away from the New York City limits, the cities shrink into towns and small communities. Some are little more than villages. By the time you reach Montauk, at the island's easternmost shore, you'll find a mere 4,000 local residents living there year-round.

It was near one of these unexpected rural enclaves in early 1957 that our story takes place. Driving home from a cousin's house on Long Island late one night—or, more accurately, early one morning—Savalas noticed that his gas tank was almost empty. Please, he thought, don't run out of gas! It was 3 a.m., long after sensible people on that part of the island were in bed. And it was pouring down rain. If only he could make it the last few miles home! But then the engine started to sputter. He was riding on fumes.

Slowly he eased his car onto the shoulder of the road as the engine died. Pulling his shirt collar up over his head, he got out into the downpour. His eyes searched down the lonely stretch, first one way, then the other. As he'd feared, nothing. Except for that light.

Although he could hardly make it out through the rain, way off in the distance was a red neon sign. Then he remembered: He had passed a diner on the way to his cousin's. That must be it! He started out on a soggy jog toward the glow.

When he got to the diner, his heart sank. In those days many roadside stores had gas pumps out front, and he had hoped he might find one standing by the diner. But no such luck. Worse yet: There were no cars out front. Sure, the lights were on, but was the place open?

Shaking his clothes, Savalas stepped inside onto the linoleum floor. It was a typical 1950s diner: a long counter with stools across from the entrance and the usual rows of red-backed booths. Through the small window to the kitchen, Telly could see a man at the grill wearing a small white paper hat and a grease-soaked apron. A lone waiter stood behind the counter reading. Otherwise the diner was completely empty. Little wonder, thought Savalas. Who in his right mind would be out at this time of night in this weather?

"Can I help you?"

Yes, Savalas said, and, without going into detail he asked if there was an all-night gas station anywhere in the area. The waiter gave Savalas directions to a garage less than a mile down the road.

"I'd be happy to give you a lift myself," the counter kid offered, "but as you can see, it's just me and the guy in back. Good luck, though." With that, having decided that the soaked man standing in front of him wasn't going to stay long enough even for a hot cup of coffee, the waiter turned back to his magazine.

Savalas walked back into the rain. Already soaked, he started to run in the direction the young man had pointed. He had gotten only a few blocks, however, when a long, sleek black Cadillac pulled up beside him, slowed, and stopped.

With all the rain streaming down the car's windows, Savalas could barely tell that anyone was inside. But then the driver slowly rolled down a window and shouted, "Do you need a lift?"

Telly wasn't used to hitchhiking, and he wasn't really in the mood to deal with a stranger. But under the circumstances, he figured, beggars couldn't be choosers. He opened the door and got in.

Immediately he felt the warmth inside the car envelop him, and he was glad to finally be somewhere he could start to dry. The driver had a calm, reassuring voice as he asked, "Where are you heading?"

Savalas explained what had happened, and as they quietly rode toward the gas station, Telly let his eyes take in the driver. He was immaculately dressed in a slightly dated black tuxedo, with a crisply pressed white shirt and bow tie. His black hair was neatly combed back, and he wore a perfectly trimmed mustache. With that getup, thought Savalas, he could easily have been a stand-in for Fred Astaire in any of those old MGM movies.

Finally Telly's curiosity got the better of him. "You're dressed up pretty swanky for this time of night. If you don't mind my asking, where are *you* heading?"

In a low monotone, and with just the slightest hint of sorrow, the driver simply stated, "To the crossroads."

Involuntarily, Savalas shivered. The crossroads? What was *that* supposed to mean? Was this guy loony? Telly was beginning to have second thoughts about having gotten into the car when, much to his relief, the service station came into sight. The stranger pulled his car into the lot.

Savalas reached into his pocket to offer the accommodating driver some money for his trouble and panicked. His wallet was missing! Mentally retracing the events of the evening, he quickly realized that he had left the billfold back at his cousin's house. Not only couldn't he give the stranger any money to thank him, he couldn't even pay for gas for his own car.

Oh, well, that was *his* problem, not the stranger's. Savalas apologized for not being able to offer him anything. "But give me your name and address, and I promise I'll put something in the mail."

The man hesitated. "Just happy to help get you out of the rain. And I'm glad the gas station was open. In fact"—the driver reached into his coat, pulled out a dollar bill, and handed it to Savalas—"perhaps you can use this for some gas."

Now Savalas really felt stuck. He needed the money, or he'd be trapped at the garage until morning when he could call someone to get a lift home. But he couldn't accept money from a complete stranger. Telly agreed to take the cash, but only, he insisted, if the driver would let him repay him. Reluctantly, the man agreed. He said his name was Harry Agannis, and he hastily scribbled down his address and phone number and handed it to Savalas.

Without another word Telly dashed to the door of the service station. He turned to wave good-bye to the man who had come to his aid, but the Cadillac was gone. It was almost as if the car had disappeared into thin air.

It wasn't until a few days later that Savalas found the paper with the phone number stuffed into the bottom of his pocket. When he called, it wasn't Harry's voice that answered, however, but a woman's.

"Hello? Is this, uh, Mrs. Agannis? May I speak with Harry?"

There was silence on the other end for what seemed like an eternity. Then a clearly agitated voice rang out. "Is this some kind of joke? Who is this?"

Taken aback, Telly rushed to explain that he had met her husband a few nights before and that Harry had helped him out. "He wrote down his name and number on a piece of paper, and . . . "

"That's impossible," she said curtly. "My husband, Harry, is dead. He's been dead for three years." Then a dial tone: She had hung up.

Dead? For three years?

Savalas mulled over what he had just heard. How could that be true? And if it was, who had picked him up? Maybe that would explain why the man hadn't wanted to give Telly his name. After all, the guy was all dressed up, driving out there alone in the middle of the night. And heading to "the crossroads." Who knows where he was actually heading or why he wanted to keep his identity a secret.

As the days went on, Savalas began to feel guilty. Clearly he had upset the woman who had answered the phone, but they had both been the victims of a tasteless prank. He didn't want to call her back, figuring it would only distress her more getting another unwanted phone call, so, as awkward as the confrontation would be, Telly resolved to meet Mrs. Agannis face-to-face to say he was sorry.

He drove to the address the man had written down, and with some trepidation he walked up the sidewalk to the front door of her home and knocked. As soon as Mrs. Agannis opened the door, he rushed into the speech he had prepared. His name was Telly Savalas. He was the one who had called the other day. He wasn't trying to be funny or cruel. He thought they might both be the butt of a nasty practical joke.

She looked at the actor for a moment and could see the sincerity in his eyes. She widened the door and invited him inside. As they sat down, Telly handed her the paper the mysterious driver had given him.

Mrs. Agannis's hands started to shake, and tears welled up into her eyes. "Where did you . . . ? How could you have gotten this?"

Savalas was puzzled. Hadn't he just explained?

"You don't understand, Mr. Savalas. This is Harry's hand-writing."

Stunned, Telly objected. That couldn't be possible. Then, as Savalas described the man who had given him a lift, his wardrobe, and the car, Mrs. Agannis stood. Without a word, almost as if in a trance, she walked across the room and removed a well-worn album from a weathered bookcase. She sat down next to Savalas and started to flip through the pictures. "This was my Harry."

Savalas recognized him instantly. It was the same man, proudly standing next to a black, shiny Cadillac.

In a soft, dreamlike voice, she told her story:

"Harry died in that car three years ago. He had been at a party, wearing that musty old tuxedo of his, and he was driving home around three in the morning. Out at the crossroads, about a mile down the road from where that gas station is that you mentioned, his car was hit by a truck, and my Harry was killed."

The two then sat speechless, considering the implications of what she had just told him. The conclusion was inescapable: For at least one night, Harry had returned. A phantom driver had paused just long enough to give a hitchhiker a hand before returning to his destiny at the crossroads.

Had it happened before? And would Harry ever return to help anyone else? Savalas was never to find out, for he swore to himself at that moment—and kept his promise—never to accept a ride on that haunted highway again.

Chapter 17
The Curse of
Little Bastard

Just another celebrity death. But is it possible that the car in which James Dean was fatally injured was actually responsible for the accident? Could the car have been cursed or even, as some suggest, possessed by an evil spirit? After Dean died, the car was involved in several other deaths and injuries. Is it possible that they weren't all merely accidents? You be the judge.

Flat. Flat for as far as the eye could see. Fresh off filming his last scenes for *Giant*, the twenty-four-year-old movie star was finally free—free to drive as fast as he dared and his wheels could carry him.

Here, over the Grapevine through the narrow mountainous pass north of Los Angeles, California's Central Valley lay wide out in front of James Dean. This was migrant-worker territory: Dean could see them out sweating in the fields as they picked crops under the unforgiving midday sun. Not for me, thought Dean. He wanted his life to be full and fast.

He zoomed past the dusty farming community of Bakersfield. In the passenger seat beside him, Dean's mechanic Rolf Wutherich smiled. The silver Porsche 550 Spyder was only one of ninety made. Wutherich knew what the machine was capable of and was eager to see Dean test its limits. Wutherich had just finished checking out the Porsche that morning back at Competition Motors, readying it for the racing event in Salinas to which they were headed.

"Should we load it on the trailer, then?" the mechanic had asked. The engine had been fine-tuned, and he didn't want to risk overheating it with a long drive up the coast.

"Nah," said Dean. "I want a little more time to get used to her before the race. I have to see what she can do."

Dean had always had a fascination with speed. As soon as he had landed his breakout role of Cal Trask, the rebellious son of a domineering, disapproving father in *East of Eden*, Dean bought his first sports car, a bright red MG TD. He also bought a station wagon, the white Ford Country Squire Woody that was now bringing up his rear. Normally the wagon would have been towing the Spyder to Salinas instead of pulling the empty flatbed. But Bill Hickman, a friend and stunt man from *Giant*, had agreed to drive it to the speedway, and Sanford Roth, who was there to do a photo spread on Dean and the race, was along for the ride.

Dean's car had been customized by George Barris, who would become famous for his modifications of racing cars and hot rods (as well as his design for TV's Batmobile). The silver body of Dean's Spyder was set off with red stripes over its rear wheel wells, the seats were Scottish tartan, and a large 130 was numbered in black on the front, sides, and back. The car looked so hot that Dean had the car's nickname, "Little Bastard," lettered underneath the license plate.

Little Bastard indeed. From the start, Barris thought the vehicle had a "weird feeling of impending doom." Nick Adams, who had appeared with Dean in *Rebel Without a Cause* and would later go on to star in TV's *The Rebel*, was also uneasy about the car. So, too, was Dean's uncle, Charlie Nolan. Then, just a few days before leaving for Salinas, Dean met Alec Guinness and couldn't help but show off his new racer. He was surprised by the renowned British actor's reaction.

"So what do you think, Mr. Guinness? She's a beauty, isn't she?"

"That car is sinister, my boy. Sinister. Mark my words: If you get in that car, you will be found dead in it in less than a week."

That had been September 23, 1955. Now, just seven days later, Dean was tearing northward up Highway 99. He had come a long way from his modest beginnings. When he was just a boy, his father had moved his family from Indiana, where Dean was born, to Santa Monica, California. There, Dean's mother died of cancer when he was only nine. His father, feeling incapable of raising his son himself, sent him back to Fairmount, Indiana, to be reared by the young boy's aunt and her husband. Despite being brought up in their conservative household, Dean dreamed of fast cars and acting in the theater.

After graduating from high school, Dean traveled back to California, where he wound up majoring in drama at UCLA—a move that would further alienate him from his father. But Dean had decided on his life's course, and in 1951 he dropped out of college to become an actor full-time. A few bit roles on television and some small parts in movies followed, but it wasn't until he moved to New York later that year that Dean's career really began to take off.

He was accepted into the prestigious Actors Studio, studying "method acting"—the same naturalistic technique employed by such actors as Marlon Brando and Montgomery Cliff. In 1954, after appearing on several live television dramas, Dean got a role in the Broadway adaptation of André Gide's book *The Immoralist*. He won a 1954 Theatre World Award for his portrayal of Bachir, a blackmailing Arab houseboy—and Hollywood took notice.

So it was back to California for Dean. But this time it wasn't for some walk-on. Instead, he was to star in the screen version of John Steinbeck's novel *East of Eden*. The part seemed written with Dean in mind: a disobedient outsider yearning for the love of his father. Under the direction of Elia Kazan, Dean turned in a performance that was to win him an Academy Award nomination.

(No one at the time could have predicted that Dean would receive two back-to-back Oscar nominations, in 1956 for *Eden* and in 1957 for his supporting role in *Giant*—or, because both films were released after his death, that he would receive the nominations posthumously.)

Even before *Eden* came out, Dean had given in completely to his passion for sports cars. He traded up from his high-speed MG to an even faster 1500cc Porsche Speedster. And by 1955 he was driving in racing competitions in Palm Springs, Santa Monica, and Bakersfield.

Meanwhile, Dean was filming his second movie and what was to become his signature role, the brooding, troubled teen hero of *Rebel Without a Cause*. But even while the film was being shot, Dean's obsession with speed and automobiles continued unabated. He traded in his Speedster for the vehicle that would eventually be his last: the 550 Spyder.

I'm not out of control, thought Dean, back on the highway to Salinas. And maybe if I am—a little—it's the studio's fault. After all, didn't they stop me from racing while I was filming *Giant*? I'm just making up for lost time.

But Warner Bros. knew what they had, and they were protecting their investment. Dean was a valuable commodity; they didn't want him hurt. Now, with work on *Giant* complete, Dean knew he was simply letting off a little steam. And what harm could that do? Salinas was just another race, like all the others, and the trip there was a piece of cake.

Crossing into Kern County around 3:30 that afternoon, Dean knew he was driving over the speed limit, but so what—65 in a 55 mph zone? Everyone does that. But that didn't stop a highway patrol officer from pulling over both the Spyder and the wagon, which was still following closely on Dean's tail.

Once the patrolman was out of sight, Dean shrugged off the ticket and revved up his engine. This time he really let loose, leaving the wagon far behind—much to the frustration of Roth, who had hoped to get some action photos of the young star cruising out on the open highway.

Dean stopped briefly to gas up at Blackwell's Corner, where he ran into fellow sports car driver Lance Reventlow. He then turned west on U.S. Route 466 (now 46) toward Cholame. From there it would be a straight shot to U.S. Route 1. Then he'd take the Pacific Coast Highway on the last leg up to Salinas. They were only a few hours away, so Dean slowed down and settled in. No need to hurry now. If he stayed at the speed limit, maybe Hickman would catch up to them before they hit the ocean.

Twenty-three-year-old Cal Poly student Donald Turnupseed was traveling home to Tulare, going east on the same highway as Dean, driving his 1950 black-and-white Ford Custom Tudor coupe. An ordinary day, and the road seemed perfectly clear.

Even with the setting sun in his eyes—it was about 5:30 p.m.—Dean could see the Ford coupe. Was it going to cut in front of him? Dean turned to Wutherich and said, "That guy's gotta stop. He'll see us."

But the Porsche was slung low, and its silver color blended into the shimmering roadway. To Turnupseed, the Spyder was invisible.

The student cut sharply to the left, forking onto State Road 41, and at the last moment he saw the Porsche. But it was too late. The two cars hit at full speed. Wutherich was flung out of the car, breaking his jaw and sustaining other injuries in the collision. Turnupseed amazingly also survived the crash with only a slash on his forehead and a battered nose. But Dean was not so lucky.

The Spyder was crushed, with Dean incurring a broken neck and massive internal injuries. He was removed from the twisted wreckage, transferred to an ambulance, and taken to Paso Robles War Memorial Hospital, where he was pronounced dead on arrival at 5:59 p.m.

How ironic that just a couple of weeks earlier, Dean had filmed a thirty-second commercial for the National Highway Safety Committee. Interviewed by actor Gig Young, Dean made a play on words of the then-popular phrase "The life you save may be your own." He looked directly into the camera and quipped, "Take it easy driving. The life you save may be *mine*." The words had just come back to haunt him.

With his life cut off at such an early age, the movie star entered immortality to become a cult icon, forever young.

Yes, the body may have perished, but his fame lives on. And so, too, may his ghost. Dean was interred in the family plot at Park Cemetery back in Fairmount. Ever since, visitors have claimed to sense Dean's spirit hovering around his grave.

Also to this day, motorists passing through the intersection of Highways 46 and 41 outside of Cholame report hearing screeching tires, crunching metal, and shattering glass. (The crossroads was officially named the James Dean Memorial Junction in 2005.)

But there's much more to the story. The "spirit" of Little Bastard may live on as well—and, if so, it is definitely wicked. At least two other people would die and several more be maimed before the haunted car was through.

George Barris bought the crumpled Spyder. He had no illusions about ever reconstructing it, but he knew any undamaged parts would still be quite valuable. It was under his ownership that Little Bastard claimed its next victims. While the car was being loaded onto a trailer to bring it back to Los Angeles, the Porsche slipped and broke a mechanic's leg. Little Bastard was just getting started.

The first salvage had tragic results. Barris sold the refurbished engine and powertrain to two doctors, Troy McHenry and William F. Eschrid, respectively, who installed them in their personal street rods. While racing at the speedway in Pomona on October 2, 1956, Eschrid misread the banking on a curve and was seriously hurt when his car rolled over. The vehicle McHenry was driving spun completely out of control and crashed into a tree, killing him instantly. Little Bastard's two undamaged tires were sold and placed on another car, but they blew out simultaneously, nearly causing the driver to crash.

The next victims of the curse were thieves trying to strip the car. While attempting to steal the steering wheel from the flattened Porsche, one young man had his arm slashed open by a piece of jagged metal. Later, another robber was hurt when he tried to make off with the bloodstained driver's seat.

Enough was enough! Barris decided to put the wreckage into permanent storage before anyone else could be hurt. But the California Highway Patrol had other plans.

The CHP was about to send out a highway safety exhibit around the state, and with Dean's death still fresh in the public's mind, they asked permission to put his car on display. How could Barris refuse?

From the start the exhibition had problems. The garage in which the mangled Porsche was being stored burned to the ground, destroying everything inside—except the "remains" of the Spyder, which was barely hurt by the flames. At the display's second showing, at a high school in Sacramento, the car slipped off its tracks and broke a student's hip.

Moving the Porsche from one town to another became a nightmare all its own. En route to Salinas, the truck carrying the car went out of control, and the driver, George Barkuis, spilled out. Little Bastard rolled off the truck and crushed him before he could get out of the way. Other incidents continued to occur: In 1958 a different truck carrying the Spyder was parked on a hillside when it fell out of gear and rolled down into a car. While on display in New Orleans in 1959, the Porsche broke apart into several pieces for seemingly no reason. At least two other times the car slipped off its mountings while being carried on the back of other vehicles. Shards flying off the trucks transporting Little Bastard smashed windshields on a highway in Oregon.

Accidents?

Perhaps the strangest part of the Little Bastard legend is its disappearance. In 1960 the wreck was placed on display by the Florida Highway Patrol. Afterward, it was shipped back to Los Angeles. But when the truck carrying it arrived, the car was gone!

Whether Little Bastard had never actually been loaded onto the truck or whether it was stolen on the way remains a mystery. But even after it vanished, Little Bastard may have claimed more victims. Some say its curse extended to several of Dean's associates who died in violence, unusually young, or both.

Perhaps consumed by the memories of that afternoon in 1955, Wutherich attempted suicide several times before being killed in a car accident himself in 1981. Reventlow died in a plane crash. Then there were Dean's fellow actors in *Rebel Without a Cause*: Natalie Wood died in a boating accident at the age of forty-three, Sal Mineo was thirty-seven when he was stabbed to death in a West Hollywood alley, and Nick Adams died of a drug overdose at thirty-six.

Were all these occurrences just freakish coincidences, or was the car actually cursed? Or, as some believe, was it inhabited by some sort of malevolent being—much like the Chrysler Fury in Stephen King's horror novel *Christine*? Perhaps we'll never know. That is, unless Little Bastard is still out there somewhere, waiting and watching, biding its time until it makes its nightmarish return.

Part Four

LOST
SOULS

Usually the soul passes on to its reward on the Other Side. Some, however, get trapped here and never seem to be able to take that highway to the Beyond.

　　To wrap up our survey of haunted roadways we have a motley collection of spooks, including cowboys, Indians, and fair maidens from the Old West; phantom riders on horse-back; an Irish rascal who danced with the devil, then "lived" to regret it; and a busload of ghostly children who help out strangers stranded on railroad tracks. Finally, we'll "get our kicks" on Route 666, the Highway to Hell.

Chapter 18

You Don't
Know Jack

Halloween. The night when the veil between the Spirit World and our own is thinnest, and all manner of ghosts, goblins, and ghoulies can cross over. It's the time for trick-or-treat, dunking for apples, and carving pumpkins. That jack-o'-lantern seems to be grinning innocently enough on your front porch, but it might not be as harmless as it seems. It may actually be the tortured ghost of Old Jack, the unfortunate soul doomed by the devil to wander the earth forever.

Irish Jack was cantankerous, all right. There were no two ways around it. He was ornery, bad tempered, and downright disagreeable. He was a conniving trickster and would just as soon start an argument than admit he might once be wrong. And no matter how people tried—although you have to wonder why anyone would bother—nothing ever pleased him. Jack complained about everything and everybody. It's hard to imagine a man who was more crabby, grumpy, and absolutely irritable.

Jack was a difficult man.

That Halloween night Jack wandered—staggered might be more accurate—down to his favorite pub. Mickey was there behind the bar and set up the usual pint, or two, or five. In a short time Jack was stewed to the gills.

After the usual shouting, fistfight, and folderol that was part and parcel of just about any night on the town, and with a few more brews under their belts, the gang at O'Shea's settled into their favorite pastime: trading tall tales and lies.

Jack tried to pay attention. He had a whopper of his own that he'd been saving for just such an evening, but he knew how the game was played. First the newcomers to the village, unsure of their place among the old-timers, would test the waters by rehashing a few old wives' tales. Then one of the regulars would toss in some far-fetched yarn of his own, claiming all the time it was the God's honest truth. Then it would be up to one of the master storytellers, someone like Jack, to try to cap off the wee hours with a spine-tingling ghost story that would strike enough terror and dread in the others that they'd be afraid to walk home—until a few more rounds had been consumed.

But Jack had had just a few too many. Normally, on the many other occasions when that had happened, he would feel a sense of drowsy contentment wash over him. But that night something was different. Without so much as a wave or a mumble good-bye to the boys, he wandered unsteadily to the door. As he walked outside into the nippy fall air, he felt—how to describe it?—he felt himself slowly floating out of his own body.

As his soul slipped from his hulking frame, he caught the eye of the stranger. It didn't take more than an instant to figure out who it was: It was Old Scratch himself.

"Why, Jack, what took you so long?" the demon greeted him warmly. "I've been expecting you."

Jack glanced down at his hands and arms. He could see through them! He was a ghost! And there on the road behind him was a sad, lifeless mound of flesh sprawled out on the cobblestones.

Me, dead? thought Jack. And in the devil's hands! Not bloody likely! A roar was still coming from inside the pub, and no one had discovered him. Maybe he could get out of this yet.

"Sure and it's you I thought I'd be seeing tonight, Old Nick. I had a feeling my time had come. And I'll be pleased to go away with you now if only you'd let me toast my mates fare-thee-well. I know it's a warm place where I'll be heading, but I'll come along willingly if only I might have just one last drink for the long journey down."

Amused by such a proposition coming from a man who was in no position to bargain, Satan burst into a wicked laugh.

"I've never met a man so bold as to try to barter with the devil. But sure, why not? We still have time before the witching hour. One quick drink, but then it's off we go. But, Jack, you'll have to pay for it yourself, because I don't carry any coin with me. It's not legal tender where we're going."

"Well, you're the Arch Deceiver, Clootie, and can turn yourself into any shape or size. Change into a sixpence so that I can spend you at the pub. As soon as it's in the bar-keep's pocket, you can pop out here. I'll drain the dregs from my drink, and then it's off we go."

And with that, Jack opened his eyes. He woke up, his body lying in who-knows-what in the middle of the street. But he was alive! Had it all been a dream?

Then he felt a burning in his hand. There, in his closed fist, was a shining sixpence, so he knew his encounter with the devil had actually taken place. He had to make his move quickly! Unsteady but determined, he rose to his feet. He reached into his pocket and withdrew a small purse. He dropped the coin inside and closed the catch—a silver clasp in the form of a cross.

"There you go, Auld Hornie, you'll not take me away. For you can't escape from behind the Cross, and I'll keep you there 'til my dying day."

The foul fiend began swearing, warning that he would make it all the worse for Jack when he passed to the Other Side. But Jack knew he had the upper hand—at least for the moment. He also knew, though, that (even if it wouldn't be for another fifty years) the Prince of Darkness would eventually own his soul. So Jack decided to haggle. And the deal was this:

Jack would release the devil if he promised he wouldn't touch Jack for a full year. Jack's plan was simple: Given that much time, he could confess, repent, start going back to mass, and seek forgiveness from his friends, his family, and the Church.

Now, Satan was no fool. To him a year was the blink of an eye. But Eternity was forever. He agreed to the terms of the contract, if only Jack would release him now. Besides, Lucifer told himself, no matter what other tricks Jack might have up his sleeve, the devil would always win in the end.

And so it was. Overnight, it seemed to everyone that Jack had turned over a new leaf. He was kind to strangers and generous to the poor. He showed up for work on time and always had a friendly word for his pals. But try as he might to live the straight and narrow, that was not in Jack's nature, and before long he had slipped back into his nasty and spiteful ways.

Before he knew it, the year was up. It was All Hallows' Eve once more, and Jack, soused as always and having long forgotten his dance with the devil, began tottering home from his nightly visit to the neighboring watering hole.

Then, out of nowhere, walking in perfect step with Jack was Old Harry himself.

"Did you think I'd forgotten you, then, Jack? It's one year ago tonight that last we met. If I'm not mistaken, your time is now up."

Jack, suddenly sober, remembered everything. His mind raced frantically. How could he outwit the demon again?

"Of course not. And I thank you for the year. I've used it hard and well, and I'm ready for the Next World. But it's a long trip, I'm sure, so I'd like a small bite if I might before we travel."

"Oh, no, you don't," the devil interrupted. "You can't swindle me again. You'll not be going back into any pub."

By this time the pair had sauntered beneath an apple tree. Its boughs were heavy with just-ripened fruit and, in a flash, Jack had planned his way out.

"You old snake, I'm not trying to cheat you out of what is rightfully yours. But if I'm not mistaken, wasn't it from the branches of a tree like this that you were able to wrest away Paradise from Adam and Eve? Surely now that I'm heading for the fiery lake you wouldn't deny me a taste of the Forbidden Fruit."

And Satan had to agree: The tree did bring back some pleasant memories. So with a boost from Jack, the Tempter was soon up in the boughs of the apple tree, trying to pick out a perfect piece of the alluring fruit for Jack.

But no sooner had the devil made his way into the tree-top than Jack whipped out his whittling knife. Swiftly he carved a large sign of the cross on the tree trunk, and the devil was trapped! Once again he cussed and he cursed, but it was no use. Realizing that his threats were getting him nowhere, Satan made an offer he *thought* Jack couldn't refuse: If Jack let him come down, this time he wouldn't return for ten more years.

"Ten years? That's nothing! If I've learned anything in this past year it's that time is too short for the living. If you want me to let you down, it's never that you'll be bothering me again. Not now or ever."

With no other way out of the tree, the defeated demon finally agreed.

Victory was Jack's that night. He had beaten the devil. But his triumph was short-lived, for Jack had so mistreated his body over the years with his coarse living and hard-drinking ways that his heart gave out exactly one year from that very night.

When Jack tried to enter the Pearly Gates, he was sent away because he had been so mean-spirited and sinful when he was alive. With no other recourse, Jack resigned himself to the burning pit, but Satan, still upset that Jack had duped him, turned him away as well.

"I promised that I would have nothing to do with you," the devil cried, "and I'm keeping my word." And with that he threw a fiery coal at Jack as he chased him away from hell.

Lost in the dark fog between worlds, Jack carved out a pumpkin and placed the hellish flame inside to act as a lamp to light his way. To this day, travelers around the world stumble onto that flickering glow along deserted streets and byways. It's the tormented ghost of Jack-o'-Lantern, trying to lure people off their paths until they become hopelessly lost themselves.

But have some sympathy for Jack. He's only looking for company. He's forced to walk the earth alone forever because heaven wouldn't take him and the devil didn't want him.

Chapter 19
The Highwayman

Who's that ghostly dark figure fleeting by on a phantom black steed on the highway from London to York? Why, it's none other than the most notorious highwayman in all of British history, Dick Turpin. Be careful, or he may stop you, demanding that you, too, "Stand and deliver!"

There on the scaffold a few miles outside the ancient city walls of York, England, Dick Turpin surveyed the crowd. He had been the flamboyant showman to the end, bowing to the ladies in the crowd lining the path (now known as the A1036 Tadcaster Road) as he rode the open cart from the city prison to the public hanging grounds in Knavesmire. Indeed, hadn't he spent what was left of his ill-gotten gains for new clothing and shoes just for the occasion? He had even hired five mourners to grieve for him at the hanging.

Knavesmire had been the site of executions since 1379. Now, more than 350 years later, on April 7, 1739, Turpin joined the condemned souls who had climbed those final stairs to the gallows before him. Low-lying and marshy, the muddy grounds were no deterrent to the throngs that had come to see England's most disreputable highwayman swing.

(Even today the area remains largely undeveloped, although the lands are now used for recreation, community activities, and, in part, the York racetrack.)

Turpin, though resigned to his fate, was in no hurry to end the proceedings. He liked being the center of attention. Even the guards seemed to be in no rush, and to the amazement and amusement of the waiting throngs, Turpin sat and began to chat with his executioners. Five minutes, fifteen minutes, a full half-hour later, Turpin was still recounting his exploits to the constables and anyone who would listen.

Turpin found it ironic that although he had been on the run for twenty years as a highway robber and murderer, he had been tried as a horse thief, which was also a crime punishable by death. But, then, wasn't stealing livestock how he had started his life of crime?

The scoundrel thought back over his thirty-two years. Born to an innkeeper in Essex, young Richard was apprenticed to a butcher in London at the age of sixteen. What a humdrum life for a man as special as he was, Turpin thought. But he dutifully performed the tedious duties required of him, if not with any great enthusiasm. It wasn't that he was lazy, despite the fact that his master had claimed that he "conducted himself in a loose and disorderly manner." No, it was simply not exciting enough.

But was there any job that would satisfy him? With no other prospects on the horizon, he sadly accepted his fate. He had set his eyes on a neighborhood girl years before, and, with his apprenticeship near an end, they married. Turpin moved back to Essex and opened a small butcher's shop.

And so his life might have continued, without incident or notice from anyone, if he had not turned to thievery to increase his profits. For times were tight, and rather than buy all his animals for slaughter, Turpin began to sneak out at night to the surrounding fields to steal as many sheep and cattle as he dared. So long as they were butchered by morning, who would be the wiser? And besides the profits, there was also the sheer thrill of the adventure.

But all good things come to an end, and eventually he was caught in the act trying to steal two oxen. He went on the run, leaving behind his wife and his reputation.

For a time Turpin lived in the caves along the coast, surviving by robbing smugglers and other petty thieves. Then he made the fateful move deep into the six thousand acres of the lush Epping Forest. It was there he became a member of the Gregory Gang, a band of about twenty outlaws who used the woods as a hideout.

Headed by brothers Jasper, Jeremy, and Samuel Gregory, the men in the gang at first were mere poachers, hunting and killing the king's game. But before long they had advanced to armed robbery. Many times they would break into and loot isolated houses at the edge of the woods. If the residents were home, they would force them (by physical coercion or the threat of murder) to reveal where any money was hidden.

By 1735, both individually and together, Turpin and the Essex Gang (as the Gregory crew was also known) had become infamous. The London newspapers reported breathtaking tales about them to spellbound readers, and the king himself offered a fifty-pound reward for the capture of the fugitives.

Although he was eventually accused of many more murders than he actually committed, it was about this time that Turpin killed his first man. Thomas Morris, one of the servants of Henry Thomson, a gamekeeper at Epping Forest, stumbled upon Turpin in the woods and tried to arrest him for the reward. Turpin felt he had no recourse but to shoot. After the well-publicized killing, an additional reward of a hundred pounds was placed on Turpin's head.

Yes, Turpin was a murderer. Yet here he was on the scaffold, about to be hanged for stealing a horse.

Turpin vividly remembered the evening the police caught up with the Gregory Gang. They were celebrating one of their recent heists at a Westminster inn when the constables burst through the front door. Turpin managed to escape by jumping out a back window, but all three Gregory brothers were caught (and later hanged). In the melee, other gang members were able to get away as well but, with their leaders captured, their spirit was broken and the group disbanded.

But that didn't stop our hero. Turpin teamed up with Thomas Rowden, one of the other members of the gang. But rather than continue to burgle homes, they decided that it was far easier to simply stop travelers and stagecoaches at gunpoint. After dozens, perhaps hundreds, of holdups, the pair broke up, and history lost track of Rowden.

Turpin began a solo career as a highway robber. But the most fruitful years of Turpin's calling soon began, coming by accident in a chance meeting with one of his professional colleagues.

Turpin spied the traveler from afar. Foppish and fashionably dressed. Confident in his bearing, almost foolhardy in the way he was traveling alone along the deserted stretch of highway.

"Halt!" called Turpin. "Stand down, and hand over your belongings."

"What is this?" replied the horseman in a calm, slightly bemused voice. "Dog eat dog?"

For the first time in many years, Turpin was speechless. No man had ever had the effrontery, the stupidity, to answer him in such a manner.

"You are very brave, or very foolish, stranger. I am no mere brigand." Then, to instill a bit of terror in his victim, he added, "My name is Dick Turpin."

"Aye, I know who you are, Mr. Turpin. And perhaps you have heard of me as well, although we have not had the pleasure of being introduced. I am Tom King, at your service." He spread his arms open wide, not only for the grand effect but to show that he (at least visibly) was unarmed.

Turpin was stunned. The only criminal more famous than Turpin himself was the man now standing before him: "Captain" Tom King, also known by one and all as "the Gentleman Highwayman" for his stylish wardrobe and good manners.

"Why, I'll be," mused Turpin. "Captain King. A fortuitous meeting indeed."

Before the night was over, and after many an ale, the two had become fast friends. True, they were villains, but they were champions at their trade, and they admired each other's boldness, skill, and daring. They shared their methods and traded stories, and by morning they had decided to enter into partnership.

First Turpin and King established a hideout in an old eathenwork fortress (today known as Loughton Camp) as a base in Epping Forest from which to assault their prey. They also found a cave that overlooked the main road through the woods. The pair could then appear out of nowhere, strike quickly, and vanish before their victims would know what hit them.

Turpin and his new partner may have been "thick as thieves," but King was still a blackguard at heart, and betrayal came easy—especially when he thought he had been wronged.

One night on one of his solo raids on the highway that led to London, Turpin happened upon a traveler by the name of Major riding a beautiful black stallion. Turpin forced the man off his mount and traded it for his own drab horse. Once he was safe, Major struck back: He circulated accounts of the robbery and posted handbills in the area taverns and inns. Eventually Turpin made the mistake of stabling the horse at the Red Lion at Whitecastle, and it was recognized. When Tom King came to collect the steed for Turpin, police arrested him. Turpin, who was hiding nearby, burst out and fired.

Now, Turpin was many things—dangerous, swashbuckling, devil-may-care. But he was also a terrible shot. One of his bullets accidentally hit King, fatally wounding him. Before he died, King told the constables all about their hideout and the cave overlooking the path they plundered. As a result, Turpin was never able to return to Epping Forest.

That traitor, thought Turpin as the noose was being fit around his neck. His wayward shot was an accident. To inform on a fellow highwayman, well, that just wasn't done. It was Tom King who deserved to be swinging by this rope, not him.

Although Turpin had managed to escape from Whitecastle, he didn't stop his wicked ways. He merely changed territories. He moved northward, settling in Yorkshire under the name John Palmer. In addition to the odd highway heist now and then, "Palmer" took up stealing, then reselling sheep, cattle, and horses, often back to the original owners. He was finally arrested for threatening his landlord and shooting a noisy rooster. While he was in custody the police began an inquiry about the stranger.

Meanwhile, Palmer wrote a letter to the brother of the wife he had abandoned, asking him to find character witnesses for him back in London. But the letter arrived with postage due and his brother-in-law, perhaps not realizing whom the mail was actually from or possibly having washed his hands of Turpin, refused to pay the mere sixpence owed on the letter.

It was thus opened by the village postmaster, James Smith, who also happened to be the schoolteacher who had taught Turpin to read and write. He recognized the hand-writing and informed the police. Smith was rushed to York, where he identified his former pupil.

So, here was Turpin, his short, audacious life about to come to an end. As he stood beneath the gibbet and felt the topknot being tightened behind his neck, he looked over his shoulder. Could it be? The hangman was none other than Thomas Hadfield, an old friend and once a fellow member of the Gregory Gang. Hadfield had been pardoned for his crimes, but in return he'd had to agree to become the town executioner.

Realizing that his death was only moments away, Turpin decided to end his life on his own terms. Rather than wait for the ladder on which he stood to be yanked away and give the authorities the satisfaction of killing him, he jumped. There, after twisting and turning for about five minutes, the great Dick Turpin died.

Turpin was buried in the cemetery at St. Denys and St. George in York, but his body was stolen by grave robbers and sold for dissection. Recovered before it was dismembered, however, the corpse was returned to its original grave and covered with lime to prevent its theft. Although a headstone was placed in the churchyard, the grave's exact location is unknown.

The same year as his execution, the first book recount-ing his adventures, *Life of Richard Turpin*, appeared. He was also a minor character in the novel *Rookwood*, which was published in 1834, and before long Turpin had been romanticized to the public as a likable hero. Over the next 150 years, inventive retellings of the Turpin saga in songs, plays, movies, and on television further separated fact from fiction.

And so the tale might have ended, but good stories never die. And neither, apparently, has Turpin's ghost. A spectre, a phantom horseman said to be Turpin, appears on highways all over England. First and foremost, he is seen along the A1, one of the main arteries from London to Scotland. On the stretch of the A5 (also known as Watling Street) between the towns of Hinckley and Nuneaton, he materializes wearing a black tricornered hat. From London to Norwich on the A11, especially from Loughton to Epping Forest, Turpin appears on a black horse, clutching a screaming woman to his side. (Some believe the lady may be the ghost of a rich, elderly widow Turpin is known to have beaten and robbed in Loughton.) Near Woughton-on-the-Green, the highwayman shows up on the B488 riding a black stallion. (Turpin used the small town as one of his many hideouts during his crime sprees.)

Turpin's ghost has also become an unwelcome guest at a residence in Aspley Guise in Bedfordshire in southwest England. According to onlookers, a spectral man on horseback rides up to the home, dismounts, and then floats through a hedge surrounding the residence. Others hear hoofbeats and see the rustling of the bushes. The haunting is attached to a rumor that the owner of the house locked his daughter and her unwelcome lover in a cupboard and allowed them to die trapped in the confined space. While robbing the house, Turpin supposedly stumbled onto the bodies, and he blackmailed the owner into allowing him to use the place as a hideaway.

Finally, the Turpin ghost legend has a modern twist: The eighteenth-century highwayman now haunts an airport—Heathrow! The terminals are located in Hounslow Heath, which was a frequent site of highway robberies during Turpin's lifetime because it was on the major route from London to the West Country. An invisible spectre creeps up behind travelers at the airport, breathing heavily or blowing on their necks. Although no apparition has ever been seen, the presence has become identified as Turpin.

The days of the roaming bandits may be over, but that won't stop you from running into their ghosts, including the most famous one of all, Dick Turpin.

Chapter 20

The Headless Horseman

Those old wives' tales are only superstitions, aren't they? There couldn't really be a phantom headless rider who chases down unsuspecting travelers on lonely back roads at night. Or could there?

The rustic village of Sleepy Hollow lies a pleasant ride or a half-day's walk just over the rolling hills from Tarrytown on the widening banks of the Hudson River known as the Tappan Zee. It may be only twenty-five miles north of New York City, but in 1789, Sleepy Hollow might as well have been in a different world.

Sleepy Hollow. Even its name suggested the bucolic collection of farms and homesteads dotting the countryside in which the new schoolmaster Ichabod Crane was instructing the youths of the local Dutch immigrants. Tall, lean, and lanky, Ichabod could never have been mistaken for a local son among the short, sturdy Knickerbockers who lived there. In fact, his long limbs, gangly manner, and beaklike nose often made him the butt of jokes behind his back.

As was the way with country teachers at the end of the eighteenth century, poor Ichabod received a small stipend collected from the households in the area, but this barely provided his means. He could not even afford to rent his own place, so he boarded as a guest in the homes of the children he taught, moving every few weeks from one house to the next, staying just long enough for his visit to be considered a blessing, or at least a welcome novelty, but departing before he became a burden.

Almost every night he was invited to dine in one of the many homes in the hamlet, for after the dishes were cleared, Ichabod would delight the inhabitants of the humble dwelling with "news" of the village—"gossip" would be more accurate if one were to tell the truth—that he was privy to as he wandered through the glens. On other nights he recounted one of the many scary tales of ghosts and hobgoblins that were so popular among the superstitious residents of the area. Indeed, Ichabod was so good at relating such spooky stories and told them so convincingly that he wasn't sure himself whether such supernatural spirits existed in the world.

For all the pleasure it gave him to hold his fireside audiences spellbound, it cost him dearly on his way home. For then, as he walked through the rustling leaves or rode alone on the back of his old borrowed horse under the branches of gnarled oaks and elms, his own terrors and fears of the Unknown arose. Every snap of a branch was a skeleton dancing at his side. Every hoot of an owl was the scream of a banshee crying his name. Every whistle of the wind was a fiendish witch flying overhead.

But altogether, it was a comfortable if unexciting life, as good as might be expected by any wet-behind-the ears educator as himself. He ruled over his domain, a one-room schoolhouse—an outbuilding offered for its edifying purpose by one of the rich local landowners—with a firm but even hand. Those who paid attention, learned their lessons, and helped with the schoolhouse chores were rewarded with praise, as well as the promise of a commendation to their parents. But woe be to the wicked, for their recompense was usually the quick lash of a hickory switch Ichabod kept ever at the ready for the rowdy or indolent who dared to disrupt his lessons.

Life continued its merry, if predictable, path until, on one of his visits to town, Ichabod's breath was taken away by a young beauty by the name of Katrina. Slim, fair-haired, with rosy cheeks, she was the only child of Baltus Van Tassel, one of the wealthiest farmers in the district. Why had Ichabod never seen her before? Well, of course: Katrina had already completed school by the time he arrived in the village. What a fortuitous accident, then, that they met.

Young Katrina's eyes met Ichabod's admiring glance, and she returned his gaze with a coquettish smile. True, he seemed to her to be a bit cartoonish with his outgrown jacket, his arms and legs akimbo, and a goofy grin on his face, but there was something cute and sweet about his manner nevertheless. He was certainly completely different than all the doltish oafs who hung out in the village square and called her name and whistled as she passed— especially the most loutish, albeit handsome, offender of all: that brawny, overgrown adolescent of a man named Brom Van Brunt.

It was no secret that Brom Bones, as he was known to his companions, also had a liking for young Katrina, and in her heart of hearts, if truth be told, she also carried a secret crush on him. Brom was certainly rough around the edges, but he was always good-natured, a bold sportsman, an outstanding hunter, by far the best horseman for miles around, and was it mentioned that he was handsome?

Many were the evenings that Brom was allowed to visit Katrina at home, under the watchful eyes of her doting father and mother, of course. It was common knowledge in the village that if you visited Van Tassel and found Brom's horse tied to the post out front, you should simply turn around, for beware the consequences if you crossed Brom Van Brunt.

Knowing himself to be clearly superior to such a common character, but also accepting that he was no match for Brom if it came to blows, Ichabod meekly resigned himself to bide his time until he was able to court the girl in private. With his excellent reputation as a dinner guest and storyteller preceding him, Ichabod had no trouble getting himself invited into the Van Tassel home. And by the time he had arrived there, his mind was set: He would marry Katrina.

For making his way to the house the night of the appointed dinner, Ichabod was astounded by the vast and bountiful acreage and holdings that belonged to Katrina's father. Fields of grain, livestock galore from herds of cattle to gaggles of geese, and a solid two-story manor that seemed like a castle to the impoverished teacher. If he were to become son and heir to Old Van Tassel, marrying Katrina would be only the icing on the cake.

Ichabod comported himself throughout that first evening with wit, charm, and grace, and before long he was a regular guest at the Van Tassel manse. For his part, Brom held his jealousy of the interloper in check. Despite Katrina's flirtations with other suitors—and her occasional disdain for his attention-seeking antics and her frowns of disapproval when she saw him playing practical jokes on Ichabod in the square, as he admittedly did with increasing frequency— despite all that, he truly believed it would be only a matter of time before she realized that he would make her the perfect husband.

One late autumn afternoon, a message was delivered to Ichabod at the schoolhouse inviting him to a "quilting frolic" that evening at Baltus Van Tassel's. Not realizing that this was an annual party when everyone in the surrounding countryside was welcomed into the home to share in music, dance, and merrymaking, it took Ichabod but a moment to convince himself of the obvious: *Katrina* was the one actually issuing the invitation, not Father Van Tassel. She wanted Ichabod at the night's revels! And what else could this mean, after all these months of patient courting, except that she would consent, if asked, to give him her hand in marriage?

The students were dismissed early and, in celebration, they quickly and joyfully dispersed to their homes lest the teacher change his mind. Ichabod spent more time than usual at his toiletry table that night, making sure he never looked better—or at least the best he could make himself look—because tonight was special. Tonight he would ask her to marry him!

He clambered onto the back of the broken-down plow horse that had been loaned to him to carry out his duties as schoolmaster. Gunpowder, as the steed had been named in its youth, had been his owner's favorite, known through the area for his speed and fire. Today the horse, more often than not, was simply stubborn and slow. His legs wobbled, his coat was worn, one eye was blind, and his ribs were showing throughout his sides. Still, Ichabod had to be content: He could do no better on his meager income. But after the wedding . . .

By the time Gunpowder delivered Ichabod to Herr Van Tassel's front door it was well past dusk, and the celebration was already in full swing. The host moved expansively around the room, greeting neighbors, shaking hands, and giving a great thump on the back to his dearest friends. "Enjoy yourselves; help yourselves to everything," he called to one and all.

The sound of a fiddle struck up, and the guests soon coupled up for the dance. This, Ichabod decided, was his chance to begin his evening's courtship to lead up to the big question. Working his own way through the other guests, Ichabod finally spied Katrina, holding court before a semi-circle of young admirers. Boldly, he extended his hand, and before long they were swirling to the scratchy strains of the old violin. And, oh, yes, Brom Bones was there, too, but he sulked in a corner, fully aware that he had no talent for dance. His time would come later.

After a few hours' time, the dancing was done. Exhausted, full of food, and content, folks began to gather around the fireplace as the night outside grew even darker.

It was time for ghost stories, for this was the tradition at such events. The Knickerbocker region overflowed with tales of local apparitions and hauntings, and the ability to spin an entertaining yarn was held at a premium at these revelries.

Fortunately, Ichabod had saved one of his best stories, a yarn about the recent Salem witchcraft trails. Another guest then shared the tale of the ghost of that dastardly spy Major André, who had been captured and hanged just nine years before in nearby Tarrytown during the Revolutionary War. There was the story of a woman in white whose shrieks and wails could be heard close by in Raven Rock. But by far the most popular local legend—and one that had yet to be told that evening—was the ghost of the Headless Hessian, or as he was more popularly known, the Headless Horseman.

And it was here that Brom Bones took command of the floor. Standing before the whipping flames in the fireplace, Brom towered over the assembled group, their dumbstruck faces glued to his every word. He started out by recounting the part of the story everyone knew and loved: Every night the horseman tied up his stallion among the graves of the old churchyard in Sleepy Hollow. Coming away from the church, a road led through a dense patch of forest through which ran a small, sparkling stream. A narrow, rickety bridge had been built over the brook, and it was here that the horseman most liked to ambush his prey.

Brom told how the horseman fell upon Old Man Brouwar on his ride home from Sleepy Hollow one night. Up until that time the man had not believed in such nonsense as ghosts and spirits, but as Brouwar entered the thicket near the church, he soon realized a lone rider was on the road in front of him. As they reached the bridge, the horseman in front turned to face Brouwar: To the farmer's disbelief and terror, the rider turned into a skull-less skeleton right before his eyes. The creature tore the old man off his mount and threw him into the stream. The Headless Horseman then whipped his steed, which leaped into the air, sailed over the treetops, and vanished with a clap of thunder into the night sky.

Brom Bones paused, just long enough for the dreadful horror of Brouwar's brush with the demon to sink in. Then he quietly added, "I was once approached by the horseman as well.

Now you could hear a pin drop. The people stared in rapt wonder as Brom Bones pressed on. Yes, the Headless Horseman had come up behind him as he was returning one night from Sing Sing, just ten miles up the river. The devil phantom rode up beside Brom and offered to race him back to Sleepy Hollow. Knowing the strength of Daredevil, his stallion, Brom took the challenge. And they were off! For most of the run, it was neck and neck. But as they neared that fateful bridge, the Headless Horseman dug his heels into the flanks of his charger, it doubled in speed, and then, just as they reached the stream, the spectres disappeared in a burst of flame.

Everyone in the room gasped in astonishment. Then, as one, they heartily congratulated Brom for having escaped the nefarious horseman from hell. Convinced that he had prevailed in the storytelling, Brom made a sidelong, triumphant sneer at the beaten pedagogue, then scooped up his hat, made what seemed to be a sincere apology for having to leave the pleasant company so early, and swept out the door.

The night's festivities slowly wound down. Partygoers gave their thanks to farmer Van Tassel as they wrapped themselves up warmly to begin their journeys home. If anyone had taken notice, they might also have seen a downhearted schoolmaster quietly readying himself for the long trip back to his empty quarters, for he had taken the opportunity after Brom's abrupt departure to slip Katrina into a corner and—well, no one is really sure what was said or whether the proposal was made. But Ichabod left the room a crestfallen and disconsolate man.

Ichabod mounted the weary Gunpowder, shook the reins, and started the melancholy ride home. Almost immediately the quiet of the barren fields began to fill Ichabod with a feeling of emptiness and dread. It was the witching hour. His usual uneasiness traveling alone in the dark of the night was even worse tonight, as memories of the many terrifying stories that had been told at the party spun in his head.

As he approached the forested hollow itself, Ichabod grasped the reins tighter. If only he could make it through the woods all right; if only he wasn't set upon by spirits; if only . . . And then he heard it. Matching his horse's hoofbeats one by one was the steady clop, clop, clop of another. He stopped. Silence. Was he imagining things? He started up again. But, no, there it was again. Being careful not to signal his panic, he first pushed old Gunpowder into a slow trot, then a canter.

Summoning up all his courage, Ichabod looked over his shoulder. And then he saw the apparition: Rearing up on its back two legs was a black stallion, larger than he had ever seen. Its nostrils flared and its breath steamed in the night air. Its whinny cut through the dark like a scream. And on the demon horse's back was the solitary figure of a man, tall, dressed all in black, and wearing a long cloak fluttering in the breeze. And—to Ichabod's alarm—the ghost had no head! But, wait, yes he did. Cradled in the horseman's left arm was his decapitated cranium, with flaming eyes and its face flashing a toothy, malevolent grin.

With a yelp, the teacher dug his heels into Gunpowder's sides. The horse pulled itself to attention, summoned up what strength it had left from its bygone glory days, and took off in a gallop. But no matter how quickly Ichabod and Gunpowder sped, the Headless Horseman was right behind them. Suddenly there it was: the church bridge. According to legend, if Ichabod could just make it over the bridge and past the graveyard, he would be safe. The Headless Horseman would be powerless to harm him. Madly he dashed across the bridge. The church was only a few yards away.

But then Ichabod made what may have been his fatal mistake. He looked back to see whether he would escape his adversary, and . . . blackness. The last thing Ichabod saw was the Horseman lift his head above his shoulders, then throw the screaming skull directly at him!

The next morning, word quickly spread that the lesson master was missing. Searchers soon discovered Gunpowder serenely grazing at the far side of the bridge, and close by, Ichabod's hat was found stomped flat on the trail, along with the remains of what appeared to be a jack-o'-lantern. But other than that, no trace of Ichabod Crane was ever seen in Sleepy Hollow again.

By year's end, Baltus Van Tassel proudly announced that his daughter Katrina and Brom Van Brunt were to be wed, and in the spring they were happily married. As for Katrina's other suitor, some folks say Ichabod was seen later that year down in the city of New York. Others heard he was teaching at another country schoolhouse farther up the Tappan Zee. But most people had come to their own conclusion: that Ichabod Crane had been spirited away by the Headless Horseman.

Chapter 21
The Galloping Ghost of Laramie

It's the 1840s. Would you be crazy enough to ride out on your own across the sweeping plains, far from your outpost, without a guide, without a gun? Well, yes, if you were a headstrong thirteen-year-old. The only problem is, sometimes the only way to get back to where you started is by making a detour through the Other Side.

Take someone with you, someone with a rifle, she thought as she laced up the saddle. That's all my father ever says. Doesn't he realize that I'm almost fourteen and I can take care of myself? I'm not a little girl anymore.

And just to prove it, she thought, look at how I'm dressed. I'm in my Sunday dress, like a lady. No one will mistake me for some grubby tomboy—or even a cowgirl.

The young woman—let's call her Annie—was, indeed, quite independent, just like her late mother had been. Her father had never regretted bringing the girl with them, but having deprived her of a "normal" childhood that she might have had growing up back east, he had to make allowances. When she wanted to go out on these rides, he couldn't bring himself to say no.

Besides, in just a few short years, too few by his reckoning, she *would* be a woman. She would fall in love—would it be with one of the army regulars at the fort, a trader like himself, or one of the immigrants moving west?—and he would lose her forever. He knew that out here in the wilderness, once you've said your good-byes, they were usually for good.

So when he found out that Annie had disobeyed his orders and taken off on her own, just to see some of the countryside, he couldn't be angry. Sure, he was upset, but mostly he was just concerned for her safety. Things had been quiet, and the traders were at peace with the Sioux, but there were plenty of dangers out there even for grown men with years of experience in the wilderness, much less for a little girl alone.

Annie's father thought back to how they had found themselves in Fort Laramie to begin with.

"Westward ho!" had become the cry for countless nineteenth-century settlers who wanted to set out into the unknown, to try for a better life. To that end the pioneers struggled across the vast, open territories from the Atlantic to the Pacific.

Their path was blazed by the early fur traders and other explorers who preceded even Meriwether Lewis and William Clark. In fact, at the time of that famous expedition from 1804 to 1806, most of the nonnative settlers on the Oregon coast were there as part of the British Hudson Bay Company, which controlled all the fur trading in the territory.

The early routes across the continent weren't practical for mass travel for a number of reasons. Some passed too far north through the lands of the hostile Blackfoot tribe. Others ran into the Rocky Mountains, which made it next to impossible for settlers to move their wagons farther west. But in 1810 two groups sent out by John Jacob Astor, America's foremost fur trader (and the namesake of Astoria, Oregon), discovered a pathway that traveled through what is now Wyoming before hitting the Snake and Columbia Rivers. Dubbed the Oregon Trail, this became the most popular route for those heading to the Pacific Northwest.

By the 1830s, this trail was being used by traders, missionaries, and the military, as well as hardy individuals and families. It was during this period, in 1834, that a fur trader named William Sublette built a wooden structure on the trail, about a hundred miles north of modern Cheyenne, Wyoming. The great westward expansion hadn't started yet, so the fort was used primarily as a trading post with the Sioux Indians, who exchanged buffalo hides and garments for tobacco and alcohol from the East.

The American Fur Company soon bought out Sublette. The outpost was profitable enough that in 1841 an adobe building replaced the original wooden fort. And it was there that Annie's father had brought the family to seek his fortune.

He was a fine hunter and an even better negotiator with the tribes and chieftains. Originally his plan was to stay for just a year, two at the most. He would feather his nest egg, then his family would continue to the coast. There, he could homestead. He knew how to farm, but in the early years, until he knew the soil and was able to bring in abundant crops, he could also trade for the Hudson Bay people.

But then, during their first winter, his wife had taken ill with pneumonia. After she died, his spirit was broken. All he had left in the world was little Annie—she looked so much like her mother—but he couldn't bring himself to either head back toward St. Louis and "civilization" or pick up stakes and continue the hazardous trail westward. Here, Annie was safe, at least as safe as was possible in the middle of the wide prairies.

He couldn't have known it at the time, but Annie wouldn't live and he would no longer be there to see the rush of settlers who would follow in his tracks a mere decade later. Although it wasn't yet apparent, the fur trade was already in decline, and most traders, himself included, would move out by the time the army took over Fort Laramie in 1849 as a base to fight the increasing Native American insurgency.

The first organized "wagon train" of the westward migration wouldn't even embark until 1842. From then until 1869 (when the transcontinental railroad was completed), the Oregon Trail would become one of the main routes for pioneers. It would stretch for more than two thousand miles across what would eventually become six states—Missouri, Kansas, Nebraska, Wyoming, Idaho, and Oregon.

Settlers traveled by horse and oxen, pulling their wagons across the open plains. The trail was not kind to the common Conestoga wagon, which at the time was one of the primary vehicles for transport back east. The big wagons, though sturdy, were so heavy that out West the oxen that pulled them usually died of exhaustion before completing the arduous journey. So a new form of transportation—popularly known as the prairie schooner—would be designed. Also a covered wagon, it would be about half the size (and therefore half the weight) of its Conestoga cousin.

Annie's father scanned the horizon. She had been gone several hours. All anyone remembered was that she had headed east. She would be gone for only half an hour, maybe an hour at most, she said. Don't worry. She probably wouldn't even get out of sight of the fort. But she had. And young Annie, her father's heart and soul, was never seen again—at least not while she was still in the land of the living.

The Oregon Trail, which passed by Fort Laramie, was still being used into the 1890s, long after Annie and her father had breathed their last, and modern roads, including almost the entire length of Highway 26, either follow or parallel large parts of it. Several sections of the original trail have been listed on the National Register of Historic Places and are maintained in their original condition. So heavy was the traffic over the trail that in some places it's still possible today to make out wagon tracks worn into the earth.

The sad story of the little girl who rode out of the trading post at Fort Laramie has not been forgotten, because she finally *did* return home. The youngster came back as a phantom rider. But it was long after her father and everyone else who had known her or remembered her real name had moved on.

Beginning in the late 1890s, the ghost of a girl on horseback began to appear outside of Fort Laramie, riding eastward toward modern Torrington, Wyoming, on what was a part of the Oregon Trail. Because none of the scores of people who have spotted her know who she was, she has been nicknamed simply the Galloping Ghost of Laramie.

The spectre is always seen dressed in green velvet, wearing a feathered hat, carrying a bejeweled riding crop, and perched on a black stallion. She seems to manifest on the trails near the old fort every seven years, so check your calendar: If everything goes according to schedule, she should materialize next in 2011.

Powerful emotions accompanied those making the trek in search of a new, better life: hope, anxiety, and, of course, fear. Considering the pain, the sorrow, and the inevitable deaths that faced the brave and hardy individuals who undertook the mind-boggling migration, it's only natural that the Oregon Trail has its share of tales of the unnatural. The story of the little girl known as the Galloping Ghost of Laramie is also one of its most poignant.

Chapter 22
Ghost Riders in the Sky

Many a Texas legend has its roots in the rough-and-tumble skirmishes fought in the Old West. Clashes between the cowboys who roamed the open plains and the homesteaders who sought to divide up and settle the land were common. And one resulted in the best-known phantom cowboy tale of all: the Ghost Riders in the Sky.

"How ya doin' there, pardner?"

"Really, Uncle Bill. Do you have to do all that fake cowboy talk?"

"Oh, sorry, Josh, I thought you *wanted* to play cowboys and Indians."

"Give me a break. I'm only here because my mom wanted to get rid of me."

Bill knew when to keep quiet. His nephew was right. Bill's sister had sent her son out for a full week—a century in a teenager's life—as much, he suspected, to have some time alone for herself as to "let Josh see what the world outside of New York City looks like," as she had claimed. Still, Bill agreed to take the boy off her hands. He didn't get to see him all that often. But what did he think he was doing, trying to get a sixteen-year-old city kid interested in the Wild West?

Silence hung between them. They were thirty miles out of Lubbock in the deep chasm of the Blanco Canyon, which thousands of years before had been dug out by the broad

White River along which they were riding. As they looked over the breathtaking view, Bill slyly ventured, "But admit it: You're enjoying yourself at least a little, aren't you?" He shot a huge grin at the boy, who couldn't help but smile back. Maybe his uncle wasn't all that bad.

"Okay. Maybe just a little."

They slowly rode the river trail, watching as the sinking sun began to cast shadows along the layered canyon walls towering high over their heads. As they watched, it changed colors from burnt oranges into deep crimsons.

"Uncle Bill, you grew up in the city with Mom. Whatever made you move way out here?"

How could he explain it to a boy who had always lived in the hustle of Manhattan and spent his whole life texting and playing video games what the attraction was for him in the Texas Panhandle?

"Well, have you ever wanted to just get away from everything? And everybody?" (Yes, thought Josh, *that* I understand.) "Well, everything here is just so wide open. You have space. And people let you alone, if that's what you want. You can make your own little world out here. Sure, it's kinda hard to find a Korean deli open at three in the morning. And we're not exactly a major stop on concert tours. Still, it has its points.

"And, then, there are the stories."

"Stories?"

How to begin? Bill had been fascinated by shoot-'em-ups and tales of the Wild West ever since he was a little boy. When he'd moved to Texas in his late twenties, he started collecting yarns about the legendary outlaws and bandits who roamed the Southwest. People like Jesse James, Wyatt Earp, Butch Cassidy . . .

And the ghosts.

"Well, you see that mesa way down the canyon a piece? The one there, where the river splits? Well, on that chunk of land between the White River and the McNeil Branch one of the great mysteries—well, tragedies—occurred in the Old West. See how the hill rises up 'til it reaches that tall, flat mesa? Back around 1889 there were fifteen hundred head of Texas longhorn grazing up there. Something spooked them. Nobody knows what. Sometimes it doesn't take much with cattle. But they started to stampede, and before anyone could stop them, all fifteen hundred of them had plummeted over a hundred-foot cliff at the other end of the mesa. Every last one of them died.

"But that was only the beginning. Most of the valleys and canyons out here are pretty desolate. Even today only a few people actually live here, and you come across long-abandoned houses all the time. Well, the cowboys and the ranch owners were used to letting their herds roam freely over thousands of acres. In fact, the cattle trails like the one we're riding on now were blazed by the early ranchers. They followed the herds on them and later used the paths to drive the cattle to market, sometimes all the way up to Kansas. Many of the old cattle trails were paved over and became the highways we drive on today.

"Then the homesteaders—farmers—started moving in, staking claims, and fencing in the land. It was only natural that the two sides started to fight. So when the stupid cattle all killed themselves by running off the cliff, the ranchers felt they had to blame somebody. Or maybe they just wanted an excuse. But they rounded up a nearby farmer and, although there was no proof—they didn't need any back in those days—they blamed him for causing the stampede.

"The cattlemen tied the farmer to a horse, blindfolded the animal, and drove them both over that same cliff. That, too, might have been the end of the grisly tale, but according to the legend, within two years the ghosts of the cattle began to appear, stampeding across the mesa at night. Some say that a phantom on horseback—the homesteader's ghost—can also be seen riding beside the herd."

Wow, thought Josh. A real-life ghost story. Out here in Texas.

"Have you ever seen them, Uncle Bill?"

"Well, no, Josh. Not them. But I have seen the Ghost Riders in the Sky."

Josh was hooked, and Bill knew it. All he had to do was reel the boy in. To be honest, he had never seen the phantom riders, but he had seen some puffy, fast-moving clouds sweeping over the plains several times. If he had squinted hard enough, maybe they could have been the Ghost Riders. But it didn't matter whether it was the truth, a white lie, or just an exaggeration. He had a ghost story to tell.

"Josh, this is probably the most famous Texas story ever, and it goes back to the 1870s. Are you sure you want to hear it?"

Bill didn't need an answer. He could see the eager expression in his nephew's eyes. If the boy had had any second thoughts about coming to visit his uncle in Texas or missing out on a week of summer or hanging with his friends in the city, they were now forgotten.

"Well, a rancher was moving his cattle across the plains of Texas up to the stockyards in Abilene. He used the same trail every year, but this one time, somewhere northwest of San Antonio along the Neches River, or the Rio Nueces as it was called then, the cattle drive ran into a new farmhouse that was blocking the normal route. Where they normally had their herd ford the river, the ranch hands came across a fence blocking their way. And, just beyond, there was an angry farmer threatening them with his shotgun. Well, that didn't stop the cowhands. Remember, these were lawless times. Rather than try to divert the three thousand head of cattle around the homestead, they drove the herd in a stampede straight across the property, smashing the fence, flattening the house, and killing the farmer and his whole family.

"It's said that within five years, the owner of the cattle and all of his ranch hands died, always in some violent or unnatural way. Then, before long, just like the phantom longhorns up there on the mesa, the ghosts of a huge herd of cattle began to appear in the sky above the prairies all over Texas. Following close behind them are the spectres of dozens of cowboys, who are damned for eternity for what they did to the homesteader. Sometimes the procession is completely silent. Other times you can hear the terrified screams of the farmer and his wife and children. Some people have reported seeing the herd trampling on the ground first, with their hooves thundering and kicking up dust, before rising up into the sky and vanishing into the clouds. Everyone calls the cowboys the Ghost Riders in the Sky."

"Sure, right," Josh challenged his uncle. "If you saw them, what did they look like?"

"Well, according to most people, the cattle have red eyes, black horns, and steel hooves, and they're snorting fire. Their brands are still flaming, and you can see them sizzling into their flesh. The phantom cowboys have gaunt faces, like skeletons, and empty eyes."

Bill paused. He wanted to throw in the normal kicker to the legend: It's said that as the Ghost Riders are passing overhead, one of them pauses just long enough to stare down at the astonished onlooker to tell him to mend his wicked ways. Otherwise, he'll be doomed to join the riders after he dies. But Bill knew that would be a bit too much for the boy, and it would break the spell he had been so carefully weaving.

So instead he admitted, "But the ones I saw were pretty tame. Who knows? Maybe I was just seeing some clouds. I've been known to let my imagination get the better of me."

The long day had come to an end. Dusk was falling fast, and the pair had to turn around to get their horses back to the trailer for the ride back to Bill's ranch. But before they did, Josh gazed one last time down the White River. The mesa was now a dark silhouette against the sun-streaked sky. Scarlet and purple clouds swept by overhead. Did that one look like a rider on horseback? Before he had to go back to New York, maybe he'd have another chance to get out here on the prairie. And if he was lucky, maybe he'd get to see the Ghost Riders for himself.

Chapter 23
The Ghost Lights

The flatland of West Texas spread out under a canvas of stars. Ten miles from the closest town, a solitary visitor peered up into the inky sky. He watched and waited, alone in the dark. It had taken him forever to get this far. Was it worth it? Would the celebrated ghost lights materialize for him that night?

There they are! Standing on the side of Highway 90 outside Marfa, Texas, Ben could see reddish-yellow orbs rise from the prairie flats. They were far off to the southwest, out in the direction of Chinati Peak. Some nights, especially around Labor Day when the town held its annual Marfa Lights Festival, this place was swarming with people hoping to catch a glimpse of the baffling orbs. But tonight, remarkably, he was alone.

Ben was lucky. The Marfa lights didn't appear every night. But there they were, clusters of glowing orbs floating maybe five feet above the desert floor. As he stared, entranced, the balls of shimmering light moved horizontally along the ground. Then suddenly they separated and shot in different directions.

From where Ben was on Mitchell Flat, it was hard to judge their size, since there was no real frame of reference out there. Most of the globes seemed about the size of basketballs, but they were at such a distance they could even have been ten feet or more in diameter. He watched spellbound as the sparkling spheres grouped into pairs, or merged, only to break apart again. For a time they'd glow brightly, then fade almost into nothing. Some would suddenly vanish, only to reappear a few moments later.

The viewing stand where Ben stood was nine miles east of Marfa, about a third of the way to Alpine. It hadn't been easy to get there. The nearest major airport was in El Paso, two hundred miles to the west. Then it was a seemingly endless drive across the deserted high Chihuahuan Desert plateau until he reached Marfa.

The town wasn't known just for the mystery lights, of course. In 1955 the classic movie *Giant,* starring Rock Hudson, Elizabeth Taylor, and James Dean (the subject of his own ghost story), was shot there. More recently, *There Will Be Blood* was filmed in and around Marfa. But the town's origin was much more humble.

Founded as a water stop for the Southern Pacific Railroad in the 1880s, Marfa has always depended on cattle and farming. During World War II, a military base was established there to train Army Air Corp pilots. In fact, the viewing stand from which Ben was watching the ghost lights was very close to the old base at Fort Russell, which had closed in 1945. Marfa was also a gateway to Big Bend National Park, located along the Rio Grande about a hundred miles south. But with each passing year the fame of the Marfa lights brought more and more tourists interested in the supernatural to the small town.

Ben had researched as much as he could about the lights before he arrived. Supposedly, wagons trains had seen odd, unexplainable lights along the Chihuahua Trail heading into the Big Bend area in the 1840s, but there were so many unfriendly Apache Indians there that no one dared leave the path to investigate.

The first written report of a sighting north of the Rio Grande dates back to 1883. A young ranch hand named

Robert Reed Ellison was driving his cattle about eight miles west from Alpine toward the Paisano Pass when he saw glistening lights far ahead. He assumed at the time that he was seeing the campfires of Apaches, but when he and his friends checked out the area the next morning they couldn't find any evidence of anyone having recently camped or even traveled through the area.

Over the next several years, more and more cowboys caught sight of the ghost lights all along the high desert and up into the Chinati Mountains between Marfa and Presidio. As Marfa grew, especially in the first decades of the twentieth century, hundreds of Presidio County residents saw them. The lights appeared throughout the year, in all sorts of weather conditions.

As tempted as Ben was to take his four-wheel drive out across the flats to try to get closer to the orbs, he knew how reckless that would be. The terrain was unpredictable, and at night, with only two headlights cutting through the pitch darkness, chances were good that he'd fall into a gulley, hit a boulder, or break an axle. Besides, these days everything for miles around was private property, and the owners could get pretty disagreeable if people wandered out there without their permission. The local ranchers had gotten tired of trespassers, which is why, at their request, the Texas Highway Department had built the viewing stand.

Over the years many people *had* ventured across the desert at night, both by land and air, trying to capture—or at least get close to—the Marfa lights, and the glowing orbs had been photographed and filmed on numerous occasions. In the end, all the scientific studies resulted in the usual explanations for that kind of phenomenon: swamp gas (even though there hasn't been swampland in the dry deserts of West Texas in recorded history), phosphorescent rocks, ball lightning, air traffic, mirages caused by temperature variations, static emissions from quartz on the ground, and reflections from faraway but unseen light sources (such as flashlights or headlights from cars over on Highway 67).

Regardless of what others thought caused the Marfa lights, Ben preferred the old Native American legends. His favorite claimed that the light is really the ghost of the great Apache chief Alsate, who was denied entrance into the After-life after somehow offending the Great Spirit. His spectre was said to haunt the Chisos Mountains in the heart of Big Bend National Park. (In fact, one translation of "Los Chisos" is "the ghosts.") Many think the lights seen outside Marfa are from the great chief's spirit simply wandering farther afield.

All right, thought Ben, maybe it's all hogwash, but the folklore does have some basis in fact. Back in the 1850s and 1860s, the Mescalero Apaches hid in the Chisos Mountains while raiding small Spanish villages south of the Rio Grande. Among the Mescalero (also called the Chinati and Rio Grande Apaches) was the great leader Chief Alsate.

Eventually a detachment of mounted police from Mexico known as the Rurales managed to capture Alsate along with his tribe, and they were taken to Mexico City for trial. Through the help of a relative, all of the Apache were set free, and they made their way back to the Chisos. But the tribe soon fell back into robbing the border towns, and when the Rurales captured them again they were taken to Presidio, one of the villages they had been looting. Alsate was executed by firing squad and the rest of the tribe was separated and sold into slavery.

Soon after, glowing lights began appearing in the Chisos Mountains and on the mesas along Big Bend. Almost immediately the luminous orbs were associated with the recent death of Alsate, and the legend arose that the shimmering spheres were the incarnation of the chief's ghost.

Ben kept watch all night. The last of the lights had flickered out long before, and he knew that dawn was just over the horizon. Exhausted after his long drive from El Paso and the nightlong vigil, he was ready to return to the welcoming motel bed waiting for him back in Marfa. His lifelong dream to see the ghost lights had been fulfilled. He was content.

Chapter 24

Children on the Tracks

The tragedy occurred more than fifty years ago along an unremarkable railway line in southern Texas. Ever since, a group of spirit children has been on the ready there, twenty-four hours a day, to push your car to safety if you get stuck on the tracks.

The railroad tracks lay in a straight line, set on a low, slightly raised strip of land in a nondescript rural area just outside San Antonio. They were easy to find. Gina exited I-410 onto Villamain Road and headed south. To her left, trees bordered the other side of the rails. To her right, the empty parcels were covered in shrubs and low grass, not a house or building in sight.

In less than a mile she came to the turn. Villamain ended as it made a sharp, ninety-degree bend to the left. At that point, as the street passed over the haunted tracks, it became Shane Road. She slowed to a stop before crossing over and pulled off to the right shoulder.

Gina got out and looked across the tracks. The road was flat, but she could see only a few hundred feet down Shane. There, it curved to the left, and she knew that somewhere just out of sight the street fed directly into a brand-new housing development. The short lanes dividing the homes had names like Laura Lee, Richey Otis, Bobbie Allen, Nancy Carole, and Cindy Sue. If she were to continue on, it was only a hop, skip, and a jump over to I-37, which would take her down to Corpus Christi. But from where she was standing, with no buildings in sight, it was hard to believe she was less than ten miles from downtown San Antonio.

That being said, she was far from alone. About a half dozen vehicles had already queued up, waiting without complaint to experience, one at a time, the ghostly hands pushing their cars across the tracks. Gina had come very early in the day. She knew that once darkness fell, especially now in the middle of the hot Texas summer, there would be a line, probably extending back out of sight.

There was also always a squad car or two of bemused policemen sitting off to one side to make sure everything ran smoothly and peacefully.

But no one was ever there to cause trouble. Or if they were, it seemed that once people got there they were hushed into silence, caught up in the spell of the place.

Gina knew only the bare bones of what had taken place all those years ago. Back in the 1930s or 1940s, a busload of children was making its regular run through the intersection. There were no flashing lights, and to this day warning gates don't lower in front of the tracks as a train speeds by. Nothing seemed amiss. But perhaps the sun was in the driver's eyes, or the afternoon heat rising off the tarred railroad ties made it too hazy to see the engine off in the distance. Whatever the reason, the driver couldn't tell that a train was barreling down on them, and the bus started over the tracks—and stalled halfway across.

The impact was fast and catastrophic. The train smashed into the side of the bus, pushing it several hundred yards down the tracks before pushing it off to one side in a tortured mass of crumpled steel. All ten children aboard as well as the bus driver were killed. Today those kids are memorialized nearby. Their names? Laura Lee, Richey Otis, Bobbie Allen . . .

To the community, the tragedy was unforgettable. And to the students on that ill-fated bus, it's also, in a sense, everlasting. To this day it's said that if you stop your car on the tracks, even voluntarily, the ghosts of those children will push your car to safety to prevent the horror that had killed them from ever happening again. And if you're brave enough to dust the back of your car with talcum powder before making the crossing, afterward you'll find tiny phantom handprints on your trunk and bumper.

Gina drove across the tracks and got into line. She knew the spectral phenomenon worked only if you were on Shane facing Villamain. Was that the direction the bus was heading when the awful accident occurred?

As she stood outside her car, sprinkling her rear fender with powder, she could see the cars ahead of her getting ready to make their move. Amazingly, you didn't even have to park your car on the tracks for the miracle to transpire. In fact, the sensation was even more dramatic if you stopped your car twenty or thirty feet in front of the tracks and just let the phantom children do the rest.

At last it was her turn. Gina set her car in neutral and waited. At first, nothing. Then there was a distinct lurch, as if some huge invisible force had grabbed her car and then given it a single hard shove from behind. Then slowly, ever so slowly, the vehicle started to roll.

It was almost like magic. The 3,500-pound Mustang was moving on its own! She had dutifully stopped the car in front of the railroad tracks. But now, somehow, the car was drifting forward. The front tires rolled up the small incline of the track bed onto the first rail, then inched ahead a bit more, until the two axles were straddling the train tracks.

This must have been the position the stalled bus had been in when the locomotive plowed into it, Gina thought. Worried, she looked up and down the tracks extending on both sides. Had the ghosts pushed her onto the tracks only to have her repeat their hideous past?

But there was no need to panic. The car continued to advance until, with a satisfying and palpable release, it rolled down off the tracks.

It was over.

Gina sat stunned, overwhelmed for a few seconds. Then, suddenly aware of the people in the vehicle behind her waiting to take their turn, she started up her car, made the turn back onto Villamain, and pulled off to the side. She had to check!

Warily, she walked along the side of her car back to the trunk. She was almost afraid to look down. But there they were: two small sets of palm prints about the size of the hands of a ten-year-old. Had they always been there? Had she somehow just not noticed them when she was shaking out the powder?

She knelt down to examine them closely. No, the prints had been pressed into the talc. Sadly, she ran a finger across them, trying to imagine the terror the children must have experienced as their lives were so brutally snuffed out. She blew lightly on the prints, and a small cloud of powder lifted off. It was caught up in the slight morning breeze and began to drift toward the tracks.

The next car was in place, sitting patiently. It wouldn't have to wait for long. The children were floating back.

Chapter 25

666—The Highway to Hell

Let him who has understanding calculate the number of the Beast; for his number is that of a man: and his number is 666.
—Revelations 13:18

Jason had no idea how long he'd been driving. It seemed like forever, but looking down at his odometer, he realized he'd gone less than fifty miles. However, half of that was negotiating some of the most dangerous mountain curves he'd ever encountered. The switchbacks and hairpin turns on Highway 666 had him traveling at a crawl. Time after time he had seen breaks in the metal railing: Were they grim remnants of fatal miscalculations where cars had crashed through the barricades and tumbled to the valley floor thousands of feet below?

With a sigh of relief, Jason was out of the hills, and he leveled off on the plateau. He saw nothing but wide, empty space in front of him. It should be smooth—uneventful sailing the rest of the way. It was late, but fortunately, he had gotten out of the mountains by nightfall. He couldn't imagine how treacherous that road would be at night.

Glancing in his rearview mirror, Jason noticed the twin beams behind him. From their height, he reckoned they had to be from a tractor-trailer. Odd, though, that he hadn't seen them before. Surely to be this close to him—probably only a mile or so back—the truck must have been tailing him for the past hour or more. Surely an eighteen-wheeler would have to struggle even more than he had to keep from plunging over one of the cliffs.

But, then, maybe the truck was farther back than it seemed. After all, they were on a flat mesa. The air was perfectly clear, with no haze, and now, with no lights anywhere except for the full moon and the endless mantle of stars overhead, headlights, especially those from a semi, would cut through the dark for miles.

Suddenly the tractor-trailer was on him, less than a quarter of a mile behind. How had the semi bridged the gap so quickly? But that was the least of Jason's concerns.

To Jason's alarm, he saw that there was no shoulder where he could safely pull off the road. The ground on both sides of the highway was strewn with large rocks scattered between the sagebrush. At this speed, without having time to slow first, simply shooting off to one side would be suicide. He realized that there was nowhere to go but straight ahead. Panicked, he stomped his gas pedal to the floor.

The car leaped forward, kicking into overdrive. He had already been traveling comfortably above the speed limit, but now he had no choice but to go faster. Faster. Seventy-five. Eighty. Still, the semi was rapidly closing the gap between them. It must have been going over a hundred miles an hour! In a flash, the truck was against his bumper. Fear gripped Jason: He was going to die!

Then, about a hundred yards ahead, there seemed to be a slight widening to the road. Someone, some blessed unknown soul, had pulled off the road at some point in the past—to change a tire? to catch a few Zs?—and the car had left behind a narrow but definite space on the right shoulder. Could he possibly make it that far—and live?

With one desperate, last-ditch effort, Jason forced his car to make a final lurch forward, just enough to give some breathing room between the two vehicles. Within seconds he was at the turnout. He spun his wheel to the right, veered off the road, and slammed on the brakes. His tires dug into the loose gravel, and the car slid to a halt.

The Mad Trucker never slowed. The semi zoomed down the highway as if it had never noticed the car at all. Jason gasped as he stared out the windshield. Flames shot out of the truck's diesel stacks, and sparks flew from the tires. The entire tractor-trailer seemed to be engulfed in fire. Then, moments later, the phantom truck was gone. Had it simply passed over the horizon, or had it never been real at all?

✛

They call them Skin Walkers. Like most tribal societies, the Navajo that populated the Southwest had shamans who were able to communicate with the gods and ancestral beings in the Beyond. They were also the healers, and it was thought that they could control the elements and foresee the future. Many believed they had power over life and death.

Most medicine men used their secret wisdom for the benefit of their tribes, but on occasion one of them might embrace dark powers. It was said that once they turned to evil, medicine men became Skin Walkers, shape-shifters that could turn themselves into wolves, coyotes, or crows that would terrorize and attack the natives.

Settlers who moved into the territories held no stock in such superstitions. Nevertheless, they were at a loss to explain the creatures of the night that were haunting the roads that connected their towns. In time, those early trails became highways, and the Navajo moved onto reservations, but the Skin Walkers never left. On that lonely stretch of Highway 666 between Cortez and Gallup, many a driver has crashed when a spectral animal appeared right in front of his car.

And if the mystic creature doesn't succeed on its first attempt, sometimes the Skin Walker will manifest itself over and over. Those motorists who have accidents may be the lucky ones, for it's not unheard of for a Skin Walker to appear inside a car itself. And then . . .

✛

The Mad Trucker and Skin Walkers are just two of the many apparitions that appear along the sinister alleyway in the Four Corners region of the Southwest that has been nick-named the Highway to Hell. Other spectres there include a phantom car that, like the deadly tractor-trailer, tries to run motorists off the highway. Hordes of spectral yellow-eyed demon dogs with sharp fangs chase after cars and slash the tires of any motorist foolish enough to slow down or stop.

One of the most frequently seen ghosts is that of a young, willowy girl in a full-length nightgown who walks along the side of the road but vanishes when you stop to assist her.

Then there are the stories of people—both living and dead—who will suddenly appear on the highway or vanish as you pass by. Sometimes a person will disappear at one point and reappear farther down the road.

Besides being a home for ghosts and other spectral phe-nomena, the deserted area has also been a dumping ground for murder victims, and there has been evidence of occult and satanic rituals having been held there. Also, for some unknown reason, a disproportionate number of fatal car accidents and pedestrian deaths seem to occur on the roadway.

Is it possible that some stretches of highway can be just plain evil? There are those who would answer with a resounding yes, and high on their list would be this one—in large part due to the route number it was originally assigned, perhaps the most notorious name ever granted: Highway 666.

Many people, especially fundamentalist Christians, say the designation of the highway as U.S. Route 666 is the cause for all the mayhem. After all, it's common knowledge that 666 is the "number of the Beast," the Antichrist prophesied in the Book of Revelations in the New Testament of the Holy Bible. And not just Christians were offended by the number. In the Navajo culture—remember the tale of the Skin Walkers?—the number six is thought to be evil and to bring bad luck.

Eventually, due to public outcry, the road's name was changed, and today it is U.S. Route 491. But you know the old saying: Once the Antichrist, always the Antichrist. So if some dark and desolate evening you find yourself driving alone on the Old Route 666, be on the alert. Don't stop to pick up strangers. Look out for any weird or unusual animals. And if you see another vehicle on the road—especially a gleaming tractor-trailer—get out of the way! You don't want to be the next victim of the Highway to Hell.

Appendix A
"BOO"k Reports

There have been hundreds, if not thousands, of books written about ghosts, hauntings, and spirit phenomena. Rather than include a laundry list of titles that can be found in bookstores and libraries, I'm providing the names of the books I used in collecting the tales you found in *Haunted Highways* as well as ones I personally find worth particular notice.

Although most of these titles are available nationally, some were issued by small presses and are stocked only in gift shops in the local regions where the hauntings take place. They can all be specially ordered through online booksellers, however, or, in some cases, directly from the authors.

Books

Asfar, Dan. *Haunted Highways*. Edmonton, Alberta, Canada: Ghost House Books, 2003. A lively collection of ghost tales including phantom lights, cursed roadways, and haunted bridges in the United States, Canada, and the United Kingdom.

Bielski, Ursula. *Chicago Haunts: Ghostlore of the Windy City*. Chicago: Lake Claremont Press, 1998. A good source for information on Resurrection Mary and the streets that border the various haunted cemeteries of the Windy City.

Brunvand, Jan Harold. *The Vanishing Hitchhiker: American Urban Legends & Their Meanings*. New York: W. W. Norton & Company, 1981. Brunvand, a folklorist and college professor, surveys dozens of old wives' tales, particularly automobile legends, while attempting to explain their sociological and cultural impact upon American tradition.

Carroll, Rick, ed. *Hawai'i's Best Spooky Tales: The Original*. Honolulu: Bess Press, 1996. Carroll has written several collections of new and traditional tales of hauntings on the Hawaiian Islands.

Cohen, Daniel. *The Encyclopedia of Ghosts*. New York: Dodd, Mead & Co., 1984. This breezy, enjoyable volume introduces some of the world's most famous ghost stories. Despite its title, the book is in chapters, rather than A-to-Z format.

Guiley, Rosemary Ellen. *The Encyclopedia of Ghosts and Spirits*. New York: Facts on File, 1992. This painstakingly researched one-volume encyclopedia is a classic compilation of ghost folklore, with an emphasis on British and American legends. In addition to information on hauntings, it also includes biographies of some of the most important ghost hunters, paranormal investigators, mediums, and their organizations.

Hauck, Dennis William. *Haunted Places: The National Directory*. New York: Penguin, 1996. This must-have book lists more than two thousand haunted sites, as well as locations where UFO sightings and other strange anomalies have occurred, broken down state-by-state. There's a short description of each location, along with contact information and general travel instructions on how to get to them. The volume includes an extensive bibliography of books on ghosts and the paranormal.

———. *The International Directory of Haunted Places*. New York: Penguin, 2000. This follow-up book concentrates on about seven hundred haunted sites outside the United States. The items are categorized by regions of the globe, then further separated by the countries in which the hauntings occur. Though not as extensive in its listings as its predecessor, it's a valuable volume nonetheless.

Ogden, Tom. *The Complete Idiot's Guide to Ghosts and Hauntings*. Indianapolis: Alpha Books, 2004. This expanded edition collects some of the best-known ghost stories from around the world, delineated by the type of location they haunt (such as houses, battlefields, or modes of transportation). It also includes many first-person accounts, a brief history of paranormal research, spiritualism, and séances, as well as information on how to put together a ghost hunt.

Price, Harry. *The Most Haunted House in England*. London: Longmans, Green and Co., 1990. Harry Price (1881–1948) was one the most renowned British paranormal researchers between the two world wars. His most celebrated case was the investigation of Borley Rectory, which he detailed in this book.

Recordings

Grant, Glen. *Ghostly Tales for Over the Pali*. Audiotape. Honolulu: TimeWalks. Undated. Glen Grant (1947–2003), a Hawaiian historian, radio host, folklorist, and storyteller, popularized the many "chicken skin" (that is to say, goose bump–producing) ghost stories of the island chain. Among his best-loved tales, which he told in his books, on audiotape, and on Oahu island tours, were those of Madame Pele. For years he owned and operated The Haunt cafe, a bookstore and coffee shop in Honolulu. After his death, his ashes were scattered at Kaena Point, which according to ancient Hawaiian myths is a "jumping off" point for spirits, a bridge between this world and the next.

Web sites

In addition to consulting books, you can find more information than you could ever possibly read by checking out ghost-related sites on the Internet. Simply type in "ghost" or "haunting" into any search engine, and you will immediately come up with dozens of sites.

It may be frustrating trying to find one to fit your needs, though. Sites come and go. Many are not monitored or kept up-to-date. Other so-called ghost sites deal more with UFO sightings and weird or paranormal anomalies than actual hauntings.

Several sites claim to have the most complete list of haunted places. Here are two of the most comprehensive, reliable, and well-organized Web sites:

www.ghost-stalker.com
Founded by Richard Senate
Author and ghost hunter Richard Senate leads ghost tours and publishes the Ghost Watch Newsletter. His site provides listings of haunted places and an ever-changing array of ghost photos, generally submitted by amateur ghost hunters. He can be contacted through the site or through Phantom Bookshop, 2989 Foothill Road, Ventura, CA 93003, (805) 641-3844.

www.theshadowlands.net
Founded by Dave Juliano
Juliano and Tina Carlson, co-directors
The Shadowlands contains perhaps the largest Internet collection of hauntings from around the world. The individual listings are broken down by country (and for the United States, by state and city), which makes it easy for amateur ghost hunters to find haunted sites in their own backyard.

Appendix B
Ghost Hunting

Here are the names and addresses of many of the specific haunted sites featured in *Haunted Highways*, broken down by chapters, to help you go ghost hunting on your own. Directions to some of the more general locations not listed here can be gleaned from their descriptions in the stories themselves.

Most of these places, such as stretches of highway, are public areas. Parks and other tourist-related locations may require a fee and are subject to limited hours in which they operate. Some, such as restaurants and theaters, are businesses and require you to patronize their establishments to enter. A few are private properties or residences and can be viewed only from a distance or the outside.

If you're planning a special trip to visit any of these locations, especially if it's a great distance away, please call local information lines before you travel to make sure the site or attraction will be open when you arrive. And at all times it's important that you follow any laws or regulations regarding visitation, especially if it's private property.

Above all, safety comes first. It's common knowledge that phantoms appear primarily at night, so it's tempting to visit these places after dark. This can be dangerous for any number of reasons. Be careful: You don't want to wind up haunting the site yourself!

Chapter 2: Resurrection Mary

Resurrection Cemetery
7200 Archer Road
Justice, IL 60458
(708) 458-4770
Just northeast of downtown Justice

Willowbrook Ballroom
(formerly Oh Henry Park, often mistakenly identified in ghost literature as the O'Henry Ballroom)
8900 Archer Avenue
Willow Springs, IL 60480
(708) 839-1000
www.willowbrookballroom.com
The ballroom still operates as an event facility. Otherwise it is not open to the public for casual visits.

Ozzie Nelson residence
1822 Camino Palermo
Hollywood, CA 90046
Former home of the Nelson family. The house is a fenced, private residence and cannot be visited; however, the building's exterior can be seen from the road.

Here are a few more haunted places mentioned in the notes about Resurrection Mary, found in Appendix C:

Bachelor Grove Cemetery
Rubio Woods Forest Preserve
Midlothian, IL 60445

The graveyard is on a small, one-acre plot within a forested area west of Midlothian, a southern suburb of Chicago. From Chicago go south on I-294 to Cicero Avenue, then travel west on the Midlothian Turnpike to the Rubio Woods exit. Entrance to the cemetery is sometimes restricted.

Evergreen Cemetery
3401 West 87th Street (at South Kedzie Avenue)
Evergreen Park, IL 60805
(708) 422-9051
Like Resurrection Cemetery, the roads surrounding this Chicago-area graveyard are said to be haunted by a female spirit.

Jewish Waldheim Cemetery
1800 South Harlem Avenue
Forest Park, IL 60130
(708) 366-4541

Chapter 4: The Prophecy
The 220-mile stretch of I-5 that the phantom nun haunted in the late 1970s and early 1980s is between Eugene, Oregon, and Tacoma, Washington.

After Mount St. Helens's eruption, the ghost's prophecy about a fiery apocalypse was widely interpreted as having been a prediction about the volcano. Although the mountain itself is not (and has never been considered to be) haunted, you might still wish to visit it if you are retracing the steps of the spectral sister.

Mount St. Helens Visitor Center
3029 Spirit Lake Highway

Castle Rock, WA 98611
(360) 274-0962
www.fs.fed.us/gpnf/mshnvm
Mount St. Helens is now under the umbrella of the U.S. Forest Service. The visitor center is operated in conjunction with the Washington State Parks and Recreation Commission.

Chapter 5: Madame Pele Pays a Visit

Kilauea Crater
Mauna Loa and the Kilauea crater are in the Hawai'i Volcanoes National Park. They can be reached via Highway 11, which runs between Hilo and Kailua Kona. At just above four thousand feet, the Crater Rim Road encircles the caldera. For more information, contact:
Hawai'i Volcanoes Visitor Center
P.O. Box 52
Hawai'i National Park, HI 96718
(808) 985-6000

Kapaho
Located about thirty miles south of Hilo on the coastline, Kapaho can be reached by Highway 11, turning off onto Highway 130 at Hea'au. From Pahoa, a ride along a two-mile cinder road allows visitors to see the destruction caused by the 1960 lava flow.

Hilton Hawaiian Village Beach Resort & Spa
2005 Kalia Road
Honolulu, Hawaii 96815
(808) 949-4321
www.hiltonhawaiianvillage.com

Chapter 6: The Night Marchers

The Pali Highway is State Route 61, the main road connecting downtown Honolulu, Hawaii, with the windward side of Oahu. In the highlands it runs through the Nuuanu Pali tunnels.

About three miles of the Old Pali Highway are still intact. To get there, take the Nuuanu Pali Drive exit off Route 61 on the Honolulu side of the tunnels. The road will fork in about a thousand feet. The Old Pali Highway branches to the left. Nuuanu Pali Drive continues to the right, where in about a half mile you will come to Morgan's Corner.

Oahu Ghost Tours, based in Honolulu, offers several sightseeing expeditions on Oahu. "Orbs of Oahu" visits some of the places mentioned in the "Night Marchers" story, including Morgan's Corner. "Sacred Spirits" stops at spots said to be populated by the secretive fairy-like Mehehune, or Little People, as well as sites dedicated to Pele, the fire goddess (see the story "Madame Pele Pays a Visit" to learn more about her). They also offer a walking ghost tour of downtown Honolulu.

Oahu Ghost Tours
Founded by Chris Spears in 2006
(808) 524-4944 or (877) 597-7325 (toll-free)
www.oahughosttours.com

Chapter 8: The Funeral Cortege of Baynard Plantation

Baynard Ruins
Located on Baynard Park Road within Sea Pines Plantation
Baynard Park Road and Plantation Drive
Hilton Head Island, SC 29938

The Baynard Plantation ruins are about eight miles from the entrance to the Sea Pines Plantation. They are open to the public and tours are offered occasionally. Ask locally for directions and schedules.

The foundations at the ruins are the only tabby structures (using building material made from equal parts sand, oyster shells, lime, and water) left on the island. The site was listed with the National Register in 1994.

Baynard Mausoleum
Old Zion Cemetery
Near the intersection of Highway 278 and Matthews Drive
Hilton Head Island, SC 29938
The Baynard Mausoleum is just as important to historians as ghost hunters because it's the oldest existing complete structure on Hilton Head Island. The crypt is also an outstanding representative example of nineteenth-century antebellum architecture. Matthews Drive, near the old cemetery, crosses the William Hilton Parkway section of Highway 278.

Hilton Head Island is located on the Atlantic coast in South Carolina, very close to the Georgia border. To get there take Highway 278 off I-95. Once on the island, Highway 278 essentially forms a loop. The Greenwood Drive exit will take you toward the southern end of the island and Sea Pines Plantation. There is a day-use fee, payable at the gate, to enter the Sea Pines Resort. For more information on the resort itself, contact:

The Sea Pines Resort
P.O. Box 7000
Hilton Head Island, SC 29938
(866) 561-8802
www.seapines.com

For more information on the island, contact:
Hilton Head Island Chamber of Commerce Visitor &
Convention Bureau
P.O. Box 5647
Hilton Head Island, SC 29938
(843) 785-3673 or (800) 523-3373
www.hiltonheadisland.org

Chapter 9: John Brown's Body

Harpers Ferry National Park
P.O. Box 65
Harpers Ferry, WV 25425
(304) 535-6029
www.nps.gov/hafe
Harpers Ferry is at the extreme eastern tip of West Virginia, at its border with Maryland and Virginia. (West Virginia didn't achieve statehood until 1863, four years after John Brown's infamous assault on the armory.) The town, located at an old ferry point where the Potomac and Shenandoah Rivers meet, is off U.S. Highway 340.

Ghost Tours of Harpers Ferry
217 Lower Clubhouse Drive
Harpers Ferry, WV 25425
(304) 725-8019
Ghostsofharpersferry@frontiernet.net
www.harpersferryghost.20m.com
The hourlong nighttime tour walks through the town of Harpers Ferry, pointing out various buildings and sites purported to be haunted.

Chapter 11: Occurrence at the Creek Road Bridge

Creek Road

Ojai, CA 93023

The haunted six-mile stretch of Creek Road runs between Ojai Avenue (State Route 150) in Ojai and Ventura Avenue (State Route 33) in Oak View in Ventura County, California. To get there from Ojai, turn south from Ojai Avenue onto South Ventura Street, which will become Creek Road. The concrete bridge at the epicenter of the ghostly activity crosses the San Antonio Creek just north of Camp Comfort County Park, which is about a mile and a half south of downtown Ojai.

Chapter 13: The Return of Mad Anthony Wayne

Fort Ticonderoga

Fort Road

P.O. Box 390

Ticonderoga, NY 12883

(518) 585-2821

www.fort-ticonderoga.org

Located on Lake Champlain at the New York–Vermont border.

Storm King Pass

Storm King State Park

U.S. Route 9W, south of Cornwall

Administered by the Palisades Interstate Park Commission

Bear Mountain, NY 10911

(845) 786-2701

The park is on the west bank of the Hudson River between Cornwall and West Point, New York. It can be accessed either by U.S. Highway 9W, which runs through the center of the park, or State Route 218 (also known as Storm King Highway), on its eastern boundary along the river.

Lake Memphremagog
Newport, Vermont
The lake straddles the Quebec-Vermont border at Newport, Vermont. Newport, at the southernmost end of the lake, is on U.S. Highway 5/State Highway 105 about three miles off I-91.

U.S. Route 322
The highway, once nicknamed the Lakes to Sea Highway, is a 494-mile east-west road that stretches from Atlantic City, New Jersey, to Cleveland, Ohio. Along the way it overlaps several other highways. Its longest section passes through Pennsylvania, crossing the state line at Chester (ten miles south of Philadelphia), traveling northeast through State College (which is at the exact center of the Commonwealth), and continuing to Meadville (thirty-four miles south of Erie) before turning southwest into Ohio.

Although the exact route taken to transfer General Wayne's bones from Erie to Radnor is unknown, the wagon probably would have entered the dirt highway near Meadville and continued along what is today Route 322 at least as far as Harrisburg before heading toward Radnor (which is about ten miles north of Philly). This gives at least two hundred miles of haunted highway from Meadville to Harrisburg for ghost hunters to explore.

Chapter 15: The Ghost Train

Lincoln Ghost Train route
Washington, D.C., to Springfield, Illinois

The route of the funeral train that bore Abraham Lincoln's casket from Washington to Springfield for interment stretches seventeen hundred miles over seven states and the District of Columbia. Although the phantom train has been reported on almost every stretch of the track at one time or another, the most active section seems to be between Albany and Buffalo in New York.

At the time of Lincoln's funeral procession, the New York Central Railroad was one of the most important rail links in the United States. It ran all the way across the state of New York, bordering several bodies of water along its route. By checking a state map, you'll be able to locate the roads that most likely parallel the old tracks. I-90 runs all the way from Albany to Buffalo, approximating the Lincoln train route, but you'll be able to get much closer to the tracks by staying on state roads, such as Highways 5, 5S, 69, 365, 31, 33, 63, and 20.

Almost as many manifestations of the spectral Lincoln funeral train occur two states further west, on the section of the railway from Urbana to Piqua in Illinois. The tracks that connected these towns were roughly the same route as modern U.S. Highway 36.

The complete itinerary of the Lincoln funeral train can be found on the Web at www.lincoln-highway-museum.org/WHMC/WHMC-LFTR-01.html.

Other haunted spots important to the Lincoln ghost saga include:

White House
1600 Pennsylvania Avenue Northwest
Washington, DC 20500

(202) 456-1414 (Switchboard)

www.whitehouse.gov

Public tours of the White House are available for groups of ten or more and must be requested through one's member of Congress.

For tour information contact:

White House Visitor Center

1450 Pennsylvania Avenue Northwest

(At the southwest corner of Fifteenth and E Streets Northwest)

Washington, DC 20004

(202) 208-1631; for twenty-four-hour recorded information, (202) 456-7041

Ford's Theatre

511 Tenth Street Northwest

Washington, DC 20004

(202) 426-6924

www.nps.gov/foth

Although Lincoln's ghost has never been reported as haunting this reconstructed theater, a visit might still be of interest. (Disembodied footsteps have been heard on the back stairs leading to the State Box, and they've been attributed to the spirit of John Wilkes Booth.) Ford's Theatre is maintained as a museum by the National Park Service. The auditorium is also a working playhouse, so the theater is closed to visitors during performances. At the time of publication, both the theater and the museum were closed for renovation, but they are slated to reopen in winter 2009.

The Petersen House

516 Tenth Street Northwest

Washington, DC 20004

(202) 426-6924

www.nps.gov/foth

Administered by the National Park Service. The second floor, where Abraham Lincoln died, has been renovated with furnishings from the Lincoln period and is open as a museum seven days a week, 9:00 a.m. to 5:00 p.m.

U.S. Capitol Building
Washington, DC 20006

(202) 225-6827 (visitor information)(202) 224-3121

www.aoc.gov/cc/visit/index.cfm

Lincoln Tomb State Historic Site
1441 Monument Avenue

Springfield, IL 62702

(217) 782-2727

Fort Monroe
(sometimes seen as Fortress Monroe)

Off exit 268 from I-64

Hampton, VA 23663

Casemate Museum: (757) 788-3391

www.monroe.army.mil/Monroe/sites/installation/museum/Casemate_Museum.aspx

Fort Monroe is an active military installation, but its Casemate Museum, which emphasizes its Civil War connection, is open to the public. You can visit the prison cell that housed Jefferson Davis as well as the quarters that were occupied by (then First Lieutenant) Robert E. Lee and President Abraham Lincoln during their stays there.

Chapter 17: The Curse of Little Bastard

James Dean crash site
Located about a half mile east of Cholame, California, near the intersection of Routes 41 and 46 (which was 466 at the time of the accident). For all practical purposes, the town is nothing more than a roadside restaurant, the Jack Ranch Cafe. Outside the coffee shop stands the James Dean Memorial, an aluminum and stainless steel sculpture inscribed with quotes about the actor, including some from Dean himself.

As you leave Cholame, the actual crash site now lies about two hundred yards to the right of Highway 46 in the middle of a field because the road was realigned in 1973. The old intersection and the last eight miles of the original Route 466 leading up to it are owned by the State Water Department and Jack Ranch. It is private property, and you have to get special permission to walk or drive on it. You can inquire at the Jack Ranch Cafe.

Park Cemetery
First and Main
Fairmount, IN 46928
James Dean's grave is in Fairmount, Indiana, which is just west of I-69 about forty miles northwest of Indianapolis.

Chapter 20: The Headless Horseman
The modern village of Sleepy Hollow is located just outside Tarrytown, New York, on Highway 9 close to the intersection of Route 448. Until 1996 the hamlet was known as North Tarrytown.

Although you'll find plenty of Headless Horseman souvenirs and potpourri in the various gift shops, there are no physical sites connected with what was, after all, a fictional story by Washington Irving.

Chapter 21: The Galloping Ghost of Laramie

Fort Laramie National Historic Site
Park Headquarters
965 Gray Rocks Road
Fort Laramie, WY 82212
(307) 837-2221
www.nps.gov/fola
To visit the fort, travel north out of Cheyenne, Wyoming, on Route 87 for about eight miles. Turn east and travel for twenty-five miles on Route 26 until you reach the town of Fort Laramie. Once there, follow the signposts to the well-maintained gravel road that leads to the old fort.

Chapter 22: Ghost Riders in the Sky
Stampede Mesa is about eighteen miles outside Crosbyton, Texas, in Blanco Canyon. The Blanco River (or White River), which runs through the canyon, splits at the mesa, with the McNeil Branch passing around its far side. The area is on a privately owned ranch.

The Neches River, also known as the Rio Nueces, runs through the prairie between Real County and Lake Corpus Christi in Live Oak County, Texas.

Chapter 23: The Ghost Lights

Marfa Lights
Marfa, Texas 79843
Marfa is located at the intersection of Highways 67 and 90

in southwestern Texas. The closest major airport is in El Paso, approximately two hundred miles to the northwest. Although the Marfa lights can be seen from many areas on the Mitchell Flat as well as from the plateau between Marfa and Alpine, the Texas Highway Department has provided a viewing area on Highway 90 about eight miles east of Marfa. A plaque at the turnout describes the popular ghost phenomenon.

For more information, contact:
Marfa Chamber of Commerce
207 North Highland Avenue (in the Paisano Hotel)
P.O. Box 635
Marfa, TX 79843
(432) 729-4942 or (800) 650-9696
www.marfacc.com

Chisos Mountains
Big Bend National Park
P.O. Box 129
Big Bend National Park, TX 79834
(432) 477-2251 (park headquarters)
www.nps.gov/bibe
The majestic, sometimes surreal landscape of Big Bend National Park, including the Chisos Mountains that are completely contained within its borders, is some of the most remote terrain in the continental United States. It borders the Rio Grande in the extreme southwest corner of Texas. The park is 329 miles from El Paso, the nearest large airport; the next closest is in San Antonio, which is 406 miles away, but it is only 100 miles from Alpine and 126 miles from Marfa.

The park headquarters are located near the intersection of U.S. Highway 90 and the Texas FM 170. (FM is the designation for Texas's secondary farm-to-market roads.)

Chapter 24: Children on the Tracks

Haunted Railroad Crossing
Villamain Avenue and Shane Road
San Antonio, Texas 78223
The easiest way to get to the haunted site is to travel about three-quarters of a mile south on Villamain from the I-410 loop around San Antonio. To experience the spirit phenomenon, stop your car on Shane facing the tracks so that Villamain curves to the right in front of you.

Appendix C

Ghost Notes

Want to learn even more about the tales found in this book? Well, here's some additional background information that might give you a new perspective on many of the ghost stories in *Haunted Highways*. Along the way, you'll find out about several more hauntings that are related to the ones in the tales you've already read.

Chapter 1: The Phantom Hitchhiker

Phantom travelers are spectres of a human, a creature, or even a vehicle that appears along a roadway, trail, or pathway, or at a rest stop, tavern, or inn. The haunting is usually associated with a tragedy, an anniversary, a sin or wrongdoing, emotional turmoil, or some other connection with the specific location.

Reports of phantom travelers date back to at least the 1600s, and they were widespread throughout Scandinavia, Russia, and Europe. They were certainly popular in the United States by the beginning of the nineteenth century, when they started to appear in American literature.

The tale of the phantom hitchhiker—a spectral figure that enters your vehicle, only to suddenly disappear without warning—is an archetype and the most common of all ghost traveler stories. Spirit hitchhikers have been reported in almost every state of the union and many countries throughout the world.

There are many variations of the phantom hitchhiker story, but they seem to fall into one of four broad categories:

- The hitchhiker gives an address to the driver. Upon arrival, the motorist discovers that the rider is a ghost.

- The hitchhiker makes a prophecy, usually of an upcoming tragedy or disaster. The phantom nun on I-5 who predicted the eruption of Mount St. Helens is a good illustration.

- The hitchhiker turns out to be a divine spirit. A perfect example would be Madame Pele, who appears on roadsides throughout Hawaii.

- Rather than hitchhiking on the side of a road, the ghost meets someone at an amusement spot, such as a dance, and asks for (or is offered) a ride. The most famous of these ghosts in American folklore is Resurrection Mary.

Chapter 2: Resurrection Mary

Around 1939 the ghost of a young female with long blond hair and blue eyes, dressed in white, started appearing along Archer Avenue between Willow Springs and Justice, Illinois. The spectre would either suddenly materialize in the middle of the road or, in times past, jump onto the running board on the side of the car. Some motorists claimed their cars passed right through the girl; others said they struck someone, but when they stopped to look for the injured party, no one was there.

Often the ghost would ask to be taken to Oh Henry Park (now the Willowbrook Ballroom), where she could then be seen dancing throughout the night. Or, when the dance hall was closing, she would ask someone at the ballroom for a ride back to Justice. Sometimes she would get out at Resurrection Cemetery, which is northeast of downtown Justice, and then disappear as she melted through the closed gates. In another variation of the story, she simply vanished from the inside of the car as it neared or passed the cemetery. As a result, somewhere along the way the phantom received the sobriquet Resurrection Mary. Although there have been regular sightings of her ever since the 1940s, they reached their peak in the 1960s.

Because of her nickname, many ghost hunters believe she must be the spirit of an actual person named Mary buried in that graveyard. The Mary legend doesn't match up with the records of any of the cemetery's "residents," however. Nevertheless, she is often misidentified as Mary Bregovy, who *is* interred there. That Mary, however, died in an automobile accident in downtown Chicago in 1934 and had no connection with the Oh Henry. Also, she had short, dark hair and was buried in an orchid-colored dress, not in white.

In another twist to the tale, one night in 1976 police received reports of a woman seen locked behind the cemetery gates. When they investigated, the police couldn't find anyone trapped inside, but they did notice that two of the gates seemed to have been pried apart, and what looked like human handprints were imbedded in the metal. Cemetery officials were quick to point out that a truck had accidentally backed into the gates and that a groundskeeper had put the handprints into the bars when he heated them and then attempted to bend them into shape with his gloved fists. The removal of the bars only fueled the legend that the spirits had bent them.

A word about Oh Henry Park: It's mistakenly called O'Henry Ballroom in most of the ghost literature concerning

Resurrection Mary, but the dance spot was, in fact, named for the popular Oh Henry candy bar. Ozzie Nelson really did play there with his band in the 1930s, but he doesn't haunt the space. Instead, his spirit is said to have returned to the house in which he, his wife, and sons David and Rick lived in Hollywood. The home's new owners have never seen Nelson's ghost, but faucets and lights have turned on and off by themselves, and doors have mysteriously opened and shut without anyone touching them.

The roads passing by some of the other cemeteries in the Chicago area are also haunted. The hitchhiking ghost of a girl described as being around twelve to fourteen years old appears near Evergreen Cemetery, and she was even reported to have boarded a CTA bus on one occasion. Another spectral hitchhiker fond of dancing was that of a young brunette flapper with bobbed hair. She appeared on the route between the 2400 block of Des Plaines Avenue, where a dance hall known as the Melody Hill Ballroom used to stand, and the Jewish Waldheim Cemetery on Harlem Avenue. Sightings of this ghost began in 1933, predating Resurrection Mary, and continued on and off for forty years. And it's not just humans that haunt the cemetery roadways: Phantom cars have been seen passing by the gates of Bachelor Grove Cemetery. (There are said to be dozens of ghosts that haunt that particular cemetery, though none have been reported as leaving the grounds.)

Chapter 3: The Weeping Woman

The spine-tingling sight of the Weeping Woman, or La Llorna ("llore" is Spanish for "weep"), continues to be seen to this day in Mexico and Hispanic neighborhoods throughout the United States. Her most documented hauntings have occurred along both sides of the Rio Grande in El Paso, Texas, and Las

Cruces, New Mexico; on the banks of the Yellowstone River in Billings, Montana; and on the streets of and along Coyote Creek in Guadalupita, New Mexico. The appearances of a Woman in White in Gary, Indiana, can almost certainly be attributed to the La Llorna legend, which was transplanted to the suburb of Cudahey by the Mexican immigrants who moved there.

In addition to the allegedly true story of Doña Luisa de Loveros, the La Llorna legend may have its basis in the ancient Greek myth of Medea, who murdered her two sons when she was abandoned by their father Jason (of Argonaut fame). There is also an ancient Aztec tale about the goddess Cihuacoatl appearing in human form in Tenochtitlan just before the Spanish invasion. She was seen as a black-haired woman in a white dress, crying for her lost children.

In modern times the tale has taken on endless variations. In some versions La Llorna will snatch a baby out of its parent's arms to try to replace her own drowned babies. In others, there doesn't seem to be any mention of children at all. Instead, she's a succubus who lures and kills young men, perhaps in vengeance for being tossed aside by a lover when she was alive.

Is there an actual ghost of La Llorna? Or is it just a fairy tale made up by anxious mothers who want to keep their children from straying? Was it a story created as a moral lesson to warn teenage daughters not to become involved with boys above their station, boys who are looking for only one thing and will abandon them at a moment's notice? Whether La Llorna really exists or not, one thing is certain: If you run into a Woman in White seeking her missing babies, pick up your pace. You don't want to be the next victim of the Weeping Woman.

Chapter 7: Oiwa's Ghost

"Yotsuya Kaidan," the tale of the ghost of Oiwa haunting the samurai husband who killed her, is perhaps the most famous of all Japanese ghost stories. It was written as a Kabuki play by Tsuruya Nanboku IV in 1825. He combined the accounts of two real-life murders and wove in mystical elements to form a story of the supernatural.

Several versions of the story have appeared in modern ghost literature, and over the years its elements have been seen in more than two dozen movies. For example, the look of the drowned child in the popular Hideo Nakata film *Ringu* (1998) and its U.S. counterpart, *The Ring* (2002), with her drooping eye and stringy black hair, is classic Oiwa.

The tale has transcended its original source, so that people now claim to have actually seen Oiwa's ghost walking the streets of Tokyo and elsewhere in Japan.

Chapter 9: John Brown's Body

At least two other ghosts not associated with the John Brown raid haunt Harpers Ferry, West Virginia.

St. Peter's Catholic Church is on one of the hamlet's main roads, but not everyone who goes there is comforted. The muffled, disembodied cries of a baby, thought to have been killed by cannon fire during the Civil War, can occasionally be heard on the church steps. Inside the church the phantom of an unidentified priest is sometimes seen walking through one of the walls.

Chapter 11: Occurrence at the Creek Road Bridge

This story is based on the experiences of a friend, Shawn McMaster, during a real-life ghost hunt on Creek Road outside Ojai, California. He was kind enough to allow me to retell the tale here. His own account originally appeared in the summer 2005 issue of the magazine *Mind Over Magic* (vol. 1, issue 3), published by TC Tahoe. For the record, the people who accompanied McMaster that night were Scott Miller, David Arnold, Bill Goodwin, and Richard Small.

Chapter 12: The Long Ride Home of Peter Rugg

This tale of a traveler doomed to ride for eternity was popularized in "Peter Rugg, the Missing Man," a story written by William Austin (1778–1841) that was first published in the *New England Galaxy* on September 10, 1824. There's some debate as to whether it's based on a New England legend of the time or is completely original.

The story is similar to the famous account of the Flying Dutchman, in which the ship is caught in a tempest rounding the Cape of Good Hope off the coast of South Africa. When the captain rebuffs a spectral visitor that appears in order to help him, the spirit curses the boat and its crew and dooms them to sail forever without ever reaching harbor.

Chapter 16: Telly's Phantom

Some sources give the night of Telly Savalas's brush with the Other Side as February 27, 1957. One version of the story, however, mentions that Savalas was just about to appear on an episode of *The Twilight Zone* which aired in November 1962. Regardless of the exact date of the ethereal encounter, it occurred very early in the actor's career, sometime when he was in his mid-thirties to early forties.

Chapter 20: The Headless Horseman

The version of the Headless Horseman legend in *Haunted Highways* is, of course, based on the famous short story written by Washington Irving, who lived from 1783 to 1859. The tale was first published in 1819 in *The Sketch Book*, written under the pen name Geoffrey Crayon. The short volume also contained the popular fable "Rip Van Winkle."

Readers may be familiar with at least two popular film versions of the story: Walt Disney's 1949 animated feature, *The Adventures of Ichabod and Mr. Toad*, and *Sleepy Hollow*, the 1999 movie directed by Tim Burton and starring Johnny Depp.

As famous as he is, the Headless Horseman of Sleepy Hollow is not unique. There are several other decapitated ghosts out there, including at least two phantom horsemen.

Twenty-four miles northwest of Corpus Christi, Texas, for example, is the town of San Patricio. The ghost of a headless cowboy riding a steaming horse has been seen there for over a hundred years. The phantom rider is thought to have been a horse thief when he was alive. According to legend, a posse captured the rustler but, after failing to find a suitable tree limb from which to hang him, they simply beheaded the poor man. Ever since, a headless horseman has roamed the roadways and the hillside of the Old City Cemetery.

Another headless horseman has haunted the bank of Lakey's Creek in McLeansboro in southern Illinois for 150 years. Around 1850 a frontiersman by the name of Lakey began to build a cabin by a small creek, but before he could finish, he was murdered and dismembered by unknown assailants. His head and torso were discovered lying near each other just outside the unfinished cottage, and he was buried near the stream that today bears his name. Ever since his death, the ghost of a headless horseman has been seen riding a phantom black horse downstream on the side of the brook. Could it be Lakey looking for his killers?

The headless haunters aren't always on horseback. For example, the spectre of a headless figure walks along the side of U.S. Highway 113 as it passes through Ellendale State Forest, just north of Redden, Delaware. The spook hasn't been identified, but people say it's probably one of the many people killed on that stretch of road. (A disproportionately large number of accidents have occurred on that section of the highway, so it has acquired a rather demonic reputation.) In addition, a ranger's shack in a deserted part of the forest is haunted by a woman who died there, although, unlike the spectral street wanderer, she seems to have kept her head.

The Headless Blue Girl—so called because she appeared in a glowing blue light—was seen several times by many people in May 1974 in Fredericksburg, Virginia. Her identity is unknown, but the area she haunted might be a clue. She floated along one particular road, Charlotte Street, and always paused in front of the houses at 507, 511, and 513. Ghosts often return to the places they felt safe and were happiest in life; other spirits are trapped in locations where they died or some other tragedy occurred. Until the spectre returns, however, it will be hard for ghost hunters to solve the mystery of the Headless Blue Girl.

To the west, two headless ghosts haunt Highway 40 as it passes through Cambridge, Ohio. One spectre is that of a woman who lived in the 1890s along the original pioneer trail that predated the modern road. During an argument, her husband chopped off her head in a fit of violence. Her ghost began appearing almost immediately, riding sidesaddle on a phantom white horse. Because she shows up at the third bend from the top of a hill on a switchback road, she's been given the nickname Lady Bend, and the rise on which she's seen is known as Lady Bend Hill.

Not far away, the ghost of a laborer haunts a stretch of Highway 40 known as the Deep Cut. During the road's construction, the man was murdered and decapitated by one of the other workers, and his head and body were buried beneath the pavement. To this day, drivers on that piece of roadway often see the headless spectre of the unlucky man walking along the street.

And finally, in Doylestown, Ohio, about ten miles from Akron, the ghost of a headless man wanders near the old Chidester Wool Mill, where it's said he was killed when he fell beneath the turning waterwheel. Ouch! Outside the village, the road between Doylestown and Clinton passes through an area known as Rogues' Hollow. There, spectators might encounter the ghost of a headless horse without a rider. The poor creature died by galloping into a low-hanging tree branch. Eventually the entire oak tree was removed, but on some nights a phantom tree can still be seen in its old location.

Chapter 21: The Galloping Ghost of Laramie

The spectre of the Galloping Ghost of Laramie appears along the Oregon Trail near Fort Laramie, but several other ghosts haunt the garrison itself. Over the years, they've been seen by visitors and staff alike. A cavalry officer in uniform appears in the bachelor officers' quarters known as Old Bedlam, and he is sometimes heard to tell people to quiet down. An invisible phantom who opens and shuts doors and whose footsteps are heard in Quarters A (once the captain's living area) has been nicknamed George. Heavy boots are also heard pacing the wooden walkway in front of the enlisted men's barracks. Some mornings, an entire company of spectral soldiers can be heard assembling for reveille.

Chapter 22: Ghost Riders in the Sky

The legend of spectral cowboys following a stampeding herd of phantom cattle through the sky was the basis for one of the most popular country-and-western songs ever written: "(Ghost) Riders in the Sky," composed by Stan Jones on June 5, 1948, his thirty-fourth birthday, at his home in Death Valley, California.

Jones recalled that he first heard the tale in Arizona when he was twelve years old. He had ridden to the top of a hill with an old cowboy to help him fasten down the blades of a windmill before an approaching storm hit. As the sky darkened, the cowpoke related the ancient urban legend and told the lad that if he searched the sky closely enough he might be able to make out the demon herd and the spectral horsemen.

More than fifty artists have recorded the classic cowboy song. The first to be released, and the best-selling to date, was by Vaughn Monroe. It entered the Billboard charts on April 15, 1949, lasted twenty-two weeks, and peaked at No. 1. Other memorable versions were recorded by Burl Ives, Bing Crosby, Gene Autry, Roy Rogers, Frankie Laine, Marty Robbins, Johnny Cash (both as a solo artist and later with Willie Nelson), Lorne Greene, Walter Brennan, and even Spike Jones (who was no relation to the composer). It has been covered by rock and pop artists, such as Deborah Harry, the Blues Brothers, and recently by Spiderbait, on the soundtrack of the 2007 Nicolas Cage movie, *Ghost Rider*.

Chapter 23: The Ghost Lights

According to ancient legends, ghost lights (also known as *ignis fatuus,* or "foolish fire") are the souls of people who are doomed to wander the earth.

Some say that the spectral lights around Marfa, Texas, are the ghost of Chief Alsate wandering over from the Chisos Mountains. The canyons of the Big Bend National Park, where the range is located, are also said to be haunted by the cries of an Indian maiden who drowned herself rather than be ravaged by marauding pioneers. In the foothills, people have spotted the phantom of a black bull named Murderer that was at the center of an 1891 dispute between two cowboys. One of the men, Fine Gilliland, shot Henry Powe and escaped into the mountains, only to be later tracked down and killed by Texas Rangers. The bull was allowed to roam free, but its ghost was later said to show up whenever there was a shoot-out in the Alpine area.

In addition to the spirit lights outside Marfa, Texas, there are numerous places where ghost lights are seen regularly throughout the United States and Canada:

The Joplin lights, near Joplin, Missouri, are visible almost every evening. They were first reported in the Civil War era. Lights have been reported since 1913 throughout the Brown Mountains, which are located near Morgan, North Carolina. They are especially prevalent in the Linville Gorge. Native American folklore says they are the ghost of a maiden looking for her brave. Others suggest they are the soul of a lost slave.

A reddish-orange orb flits about Cole Mountain south of Moorefield, West Virginia. Supposedly the phantom light comes from the lantern of a slave from the nearby Charles Jones plantation who got lost in the hills while hunting raccoons.

The ghost lights of Oriflamme Mountain occur along Highway S2 about four miles outside Butterfield Ranch in

Julian, California. Since at least the 1880s, the yellowish glowing spots have been seen hovering over the side of the mountain. Some say the spectral illumination marks the location of gold deposits hidden in the hills below.

The ghost light of Gurdon, Arkansas, appears off a road outside of town along a set of railroad tracks. Many years back, a railway worker fell into the path of an oncoming train. He was decapitated, and his head was never found. According to local folklore, the phantom light comes from the lantern of the railroad man's ghost as it walks the rails looking for his head.

Compare that to the Bragg Road Light, also called the Big Thicket Light. Bragg Road is an eight-mile dirt trail that lies about five miles outside Saratoga, Texas. The walkway used to be a track bed for the old Santa Fe Railroad. As you walk along the path at night, a flickering yellow light changes to white and then red as it comes toward you. Legend says it is from the phantom lantern of Jake Murphy, a railroad brakeman who fell under a train and was decapitated. A different version of the tale claims it comes from a hunter who died after getting lost in the undergrowth. Yet another suggests it's the combined spirits of four Mexican day laborers who were robbed and killed in the area by their boss.

A similar railroad legend surrounds the Paulding Light (also called the Dog Meadow Light), a strange, intense single light that frequently appears in the night sky above a cleared power line right-of-way between Paulding and Watersmett on Michigan's Upper Peninsula. The light hovers, moves, and changes color, usually between white and red but also sometimes green, yellow, and blue. Its first documented sighting was by teenagers in 1966. According to legend, the light is the ghost of either a railway engineer or brakeman who died on the tracks that once lay there and who is waving his signal lamp to warn away others. Skeptics and researchers say the Paulding Light is actually a reflection from car headlights on the nearby U.S. Route 45. The best place to witness the light is facing north along Robbins Lake Road. A signpost erected by the Michigan Forest Service marks the general location.

Farther north, a ghost light appears on a dirt trail called Concession Road 3 (locally known as Ghost Road) outside the small community of Scugog Island, Ontario. It dates to 1965, when a young man lost control of his motorcycle in the rain while speeding down the muddy back road. His body smashed into a fence at the corner of the concession road and Willows Line, and he was decapitated by a wire. The hazy white light (and a less frequently reported red light following it) is thought to be either his phantom motorcycle or, perhaps, the ghost of the boy himself.

Spectral lights are not confined to North America, of course. They have been seen and reported for centuries throughout the world.

Many, but not all, of the Scandinavian phantom lights are connected with myths regarding the deaths of infants. In Sweden they're thought to be babies who died before they were baptized; the *liekko* (or "flaming one") in Finland is the soul of a baby who was buried in a forest. However, the Hessdalen Lights that appear in the ten-mile valley of Hessdalen, Norway, have no ghost legend at all attached to them.

There are at least two types of ghost lights in British folklore: One is Jack-o'-Lantern (or Jackey Lantern, as he's sometimes called), who lures travelers from their path. (He's featured in one of the stories in *Haunted Highways*.) The other spectral light seen throughout the United Kingdom is the Will-o'-the-Wisp, who is considered to be a death omen.

Finally, halfway around the world, the Min Min Lights appear in northeastern Australia and have been observed as far south as New South Wales. Sightings of the disc-shaped lights that hover just above the horizon have occurred since Aboriginal days, and the orbs sometimes seem to approach or even follow people. If you chase or fire a weapon at them, however, they'll vanish, only to reappear later. No ghost stories seem to be associated with the phenomenon.

Chapter 24: Children on the Tracks

The story of phantom children pushing cars to safety on a set of railroad tracks south of San Antonio is one of the most enduring ghost legends in America today. There are several discrepancies in the story, however, that make the tale hard to believe. So if you don't want to have your bubble burst, stop reading now.

Remember, you were warned.

To start off, no railway accident, and certainly no collision between a train and school bus full of children, ever occurred at that particular intersection. However, in December 1938 twenty-six children between the ages of twelve and eighteen lost their lives in a similar incident near Salt Lake City, Utah. The grisly, heartbreaking story dominated the pages of Texas newspapers for days. It seems likely, or at least very possible, that this was the basis for the myth.

That being said, the anomaly does occur at the railroad tracks. It *would* happen to you if you tried. So what makes the car move? There have been numerous inquiries into the "haunting" by paranormal investigators, skeptic societies, reporters, and television journalists. And guess what they all found: Even though the tracks and the surrounding area seem to be level, it's an optical illusion. Starting from the tracks, Shane Road is actually on a slight, imperceptible upward grade of about two degrees. That's right: When your car crosses the tracks, it is simply rolling downhill. It may take a few minutes for gravity to kick in, but you will eventually start to move forward, all the way across the tracks.

But how about the handprints? Those can be explained away, too. In detective work, police routinely dust a seemingly clean surfaces to bring out any latent fingerprints. In the same manner, anyone who touches a car leaves behind indiscernible marks that could show up later if they were dusted with a light covering of powder.

There could be an even more mundane explanation. Jonathan Levit, who hosted an investigation of the site for Discovery Channel's *Miracle Hunters,* talked to people who confessed that, as a joke to fool unsuspecting drivers, they would sometimes secretly press their own handprints into the powder sprinkled on waiting cars.

As for the names of the children from the bus accident being used for the nearby streets, the developer of the housing project has said that the names belong to friends and family.

So to sum up, if you do decide to head to San Antonio to try this for yourself, make sure a train isn't coming before you roll out onto the tracks. If your car does get caught halfway across, chances are very slim that the ghostly children are gonna show up to help you out.

The haunted railroad crossing south of San Antonio is but one example of the phenomenon known as a "gravity hill," at which a vehicle parked at the base of a grade seems to roll uphill all on its own. Some gravity hills, such as one near New Paris in Bedford County, Pennsylvania, have been heavily promoted as tourist attractions—not as haunted sites but as places in which the laws of physics have somehow gone awry.

But more commonly, gravity hills are connected with ghost myths, usually about people who died or are buried on their slopes. The story most similar to the Texas haunting seems to be the Ghost Hill found in Lewisberry, Pennsylvania. According to legend, a busload of children died there when their vehicle fell over a cliff. Their spirits push cars stopped on the hill upward, thinking they're rolling them to safety.

Among the other better-known ghost hills are the ones located in:

Franklin Lakes, New Jersey, located on the Ewing Avenue exit off Route 208 South. The ghost of a little girl who was struck and killed by a car when she ran into the road to chase a ball is supposedly what pushes your car up the grade.

Lake Wales, Florida, located off Highway 27 between Tampa and Orlando. According to legend, the anomaly on Spook Hill is caused by an Indian chief who died battling an alligator and was buried on the hillside.

Salt Lake City, Utah, on a canyon road a few blocks northwest of the capitol. The spirit of a person named Elmo supposedly buried in the area is said to be responsible for rolling your car up the road inside the canyon. (Although no last name is attached to this ghost, his grave shouldn't be hard to find. Supposedly his tomb-stone, wherever it is, glows bright blue at night.)

Chapter 25: 666—The Highway to Hell

Highway 666 and the sign of the Beast are totally unrelated, of course. John, the author of the Book of Revelations, arrived at the figure through a complex form of numerology in which a value is assigned to each letter of the alphabet. The labeling of "the Devil's Highway" as Route 666 has a much less exciting explanation.

In 1925 the route between Gallup, New Mexico, and Cortez, Colorado (informally known up to that time as the Navajo Trail), was established as part of the new federal highway system. Roads that crossed state borders were to be assigned two-digit numbers, and originally the highway between Chicago and Los Angeles was given the number US 60, but within a year it was changed to the now-familiar Route 66.

Main spurs off of federal highways were given a third digit, so on June 8, 1931, the sixth branch off Route 66, the one from Gallup to Cortez, became the initial section of soon-to-be-infamous U.S. Route 666.

At the time, the highway was only 141 miles long. But by 1942, US 666 had been extended 415 miles to Douglas, Arizona, to include what had been known as the Coronado Trail (named after Spanish explorer Francisco Vasquez de Coronado, who traveled through the region in 1540).

This addition, more than the "number of the Beast," is probably what has been most responsible for the fatal tragedies along the highway. At places the Coronado Trail climbs to more than nine thousand feet, and the road descends in hair-raising turns that drop the speed limit at places to as low as ten miles per hour.

In 1970 Route 666 was extended once again, this time north to Monticello, Utah, bringing the full length of the Highway to Hell to 605 miles.

The inauguration of the Interstate Highway System eventually led to 66 being dropped from the federal registry in 1985, but most of the branches (including Route 666) were not renumbered.

Over the years there had been a quiet but rising objection from residents who disliked their main thoroughfare bearing a number with a satanic connection. In 1992 the section of Route 666 between Arizona and Gallup was changed to U.S. Highway 191, but the rest of the route stayed the way it was. It wasn't until 2003 that the New Mexico legislature adopted a resolution calling for a change in the number of the route from Gallup to the Colorado border.

By that time Utah and Colorado had designated their portions of the highway as Route 393. After consideration, to avoid confusion with U.S. Route 93, all four states resolved (and on May 31, 2003, the American Association of State Highway and Transportation Officials approved) changing what for just under seventy-two years had been Route 666 to U.S. Route 491.